TORN

OVERCOMING THE PSYCHOLOGICAL CHALLENGES POST-ACL INJURY

KEAGEN HADLEY, OTD, OTR/L

ISBN: 978-0-578-28398-2 (paperback)
ISBN: 978-0-578-28397-5 (ebook)

To those who are experiencing anguish and despair during their ACL rehabilitation, you are not alone. I dedicate this book to you in the hopes that it will assist you in finding your way. You are brave, capable, and deserving of respect. Never give up on yourself; with some tenacity and persistence, you will overcome this injury and be better than ever before.

TABLE OF CONTENTS

Note: A full list of references for this book is available on my website at https://keagenhadley.com/.

Thank You for Purchasing *Torn!*

Thank you for purchasing my book! It is my goal to help you get started on your path to recovery as soon as possible. Please visit my website at https://keagenhadley.com/ to discover other resources that will provide value to you and your well-being.

Get Started Today

Download my free and easy-to-use Defusion PDF to get started today. This free tool will kickstart your (or a loved one's) ability to combat the psychological difficulties you are experiencing due to your ACL injury.

Go to https://keagenhadley.com/ and find out more. I look forward to helping you begin your ACT recovery.

Yours in growth,
The ACL Therapist
Keagen Hadley

Dear Reader:

Do you remember why you got into sports? I do. I remember loving sports and everything about them. I loved the excitement and adrenaline, the comradery and friendships, and I even grew to love the hardship and grind that goes into any athletic endeavor. And, after being injured, I remember when the anxiety of playing sports overwhelmed me and removed the love I had always harbored for athletics.

This anxiety was with me throughout high school and even into my collegiate career. It was drastically compounded when I tore my first ACL playing the sport I loved the most—football. I went through many hardships that stemmed from this injury, including loss of self-esteem, self-identity, and depression. These symptoms led me to develop poor coping mechanisms and, ultimately, damaged many relationships I had at the time.

The second time I tore my ACL, it broke me. I finally had to admit to myself that I could no longer pursue my dream of playing professionally in either the Canadian Football League (CFL) or the National Football League (NFL). This lifelong dream had been the outgrowth of what a little boy had wanted during his childhood as he grew up, watching his father passionately play basketball. Football became my passion, as basketball was for my father. It was an effortless game for me, built on grit, instincts, and physical attributes that I was luckily blessed with. As I said before, I loved football. It transported me across the country, helped me get an education, gave me everlasting friendships, and taught me countless life lessons.

After my second tear, all that ended, and I spiraled into greater depths of depression, paired with poor relationship decisions, substance abuse, persistent emotional numbness, and extended periods of suicidal thoughts. Eventually, I came to realize this was not the path I wanted to be on, and I knew that if I continued similarly, I could never have a fulfilling life. The support I was receiving just wasn't enough. I was left feeling like something was lacking. So, I began searching for the skills necessary to recover from that slump and move toward what was meaningful in my life.

And that is why I wrote this book. I knew that others, like me, would need emotional support and guidance during the difficult times after injury. The concepts in this book are not as widespread or well-known as others, but they are effective, and I want to bring awareness, healing, and hope to those who are struggling as I did. It is my goal that you can use some of these concepts to learn that there are other ways to deal with the loss and trauma associated with your injury.

I hope the tools I share in this book help you as much as they helped me. There is hope.

Thanks for reading,
Keagen Hadley

Chapter 1: Introduction

"Invincibility. I have dreamed of that feeling numerous times over the last 2,238 days. The ability to do what I want, when I want. The reckless abandon with which I could perform the sport and exercises I love, and the innate feeling that it would never end. Unfortunately, something as previously irrelevant as a 1.5-inch long, 0.5-inch-wide ligament could take it all away in the blink of an eye."

–Keagen Hadley (The Author)

Apprehension, excitement, and soreness. Those feelings were palpable during that early August morning. I remember noting how beautiful the sunrise was as I strapped my cleats on. I also distinctly remember thinking that I had no idea it was possible to feel that sore. The day before had been a particularly difficult practice; my team was told, "We will run until I get tired." That statement preceded a never-ending parade of sprints since my coach was notorious for his grueling stamina to watch us run.

I was apprehensive because, thus far, I had played up to the coach's expectations and looked to lead our defense to new heights during my junior season at my university. I was worried that I would be unable to perform as optimally as usual due to the heavy lactic acid in my legs, making them feel like overflowing five-gallon buckets. The problem was, I wasn't all that big compared to the opposition. I needed my bucket legs to feel empty and ready to escort me away from the 300+ pound offensive lineman who had an overwhelming tendency to commit holding penalties (not that they would confess).

Stretches went normally. Admittedly, though, as the sun continued to rise, I did have a few daydreams of how blissful it would be to spend a quiet morning in bed. I was able to warm up and actually felt pretty solid, despite the copious number of sprints this two-a-day-filled week had included. It seemed to be a standard day with the usual routine. The offense and defense split up, completed individual drills, and prepared for the oncoming scrimmage.

Following individual drills, all the positions on defense came together and practiced various drills, techniques, and plays necessary for gameday. To this day, I can remember how great I felt during the pursuit drill. In this drill, a "rabbit" or second-string/younger defensive player would pretend to catch a ball on the sideline and run down the field. The objective was to take the appropriate angle (from your position's starting point) and catch the player to prevent a touchdown. Most people hated the drill due to the amount of running. Honestly, I loved it. I had spent my entire life (as a bigger guy) developing my speed, and it felt great to open up and use it. There is truly a feeling of freedom and power that comes from being able to do what we love and work so diligently to create. I can still feel the warm South Dakota wind on my face as I pursued the countless "rabbits" that day.

It was at this point in the practice that I started to become more nervous. I, like many athletes, put an exorbitant amount of pressure on myself to be perfect. Football, like many sports, is one in which the more you think, the slower you play. This fact was always counterintuitive to me since I have always had an analytical mind. Nevertheless, it was true. The anxiety I had developed as a high school athlete persisted in college. I constantly strived for perfection.

In high school, this was not much of an issue, as the schemes and plays on defense were minimal. This allowed me to live and die by my instincts, which left little room to think. In college, that was never the case. Football, I now know, is like life: the older you get, the more complicated it becomes. In college, I would spend hours memorizing not only what I did on plays, but what other members of the defense would be doing simultaneously. This helped me to think on my feet and prioritize my instincts. After a couple of years of learning and understanding what I needed to do, I started to come into my own in the spring of 2015. That momentum led to a fall camp, where it was time to prove myself as a leader and consistent performer on the defense. To do so, I had to be perfect (in my mind). As a result, the scrimmage sessions always caused me a great deal of anxiety. Strangely, I would grow to miss that anxiety.

I recall my coach deciding to "mix up" our practice schedule and have one-on-one sessions before the first session of scripted plays. At that point, my anxiety immediately dissipated (for the time being). I was torn between whether or not I liked the shift, but I decided not to focus on the coach's decisions. I half-jogged, half-walked to the spot where a simulated pass rush one-on-one drill would take place between the offensive lineman and the defense. I joked with my teammates and waited patiently for my turn, enjoying the time that I would forever cherish. After a few successful reps against the offense, the drill was wrapping up, but a lineman and I had been called out to compete against each other for the final round. I felt good, and no signs of my soreness remained. My legs were eager to perform the actions I'd spent years training them for.

As a defensive player, your "get-off" or start is critical during each play. The reason it is so important is that the quicker you can get off the line of scrimmage, the smaller the offense's advantage (they're obviously the only ones who know when they'll snap the ball).

I had a fantastic "get-off," and the sequence went off without a hitch. I'd already beaten my opponent to his shoulder and taken on only half of his body. When I got to his shoulder, I pivoted to start a "swim" movement that was a mainstay in my attack arsenal. Only, for some reason, this time, the technique did not go as expected. I'd beaten the offensive lineman off the ball, effectively blocking his hand from touching me, all but ensuring my victory in the repetition. All I had to do now was pivot and complete the repetition.

He hadn't even touched me.

I distinctly remember the feeling. It is something that continued to haunt me for years. An audible "pop" that took me off my feet. I remember first being embarrassed that I had fallen down without being touched. Then, my mind started to reel as to why I had fallen. It couldn't be. Not me. I had done everything my coaches, strength coaches, and teammates had. It must have been a fluke; that's just something you hear about on SportsCenter. Right?

The anterior cruciate ligament (ACL). The bane of SportsCenter's existence. The ACL, as its name suggests, is crucial. Both of the knee's cruciate ligaments are housed in the knee joint (surprise).[1] They cross internally, forming an X (the ACL and PCL), preventing the forward and backward translation of the joint. The ACL specifically prevents the tibia from sliding forward in relation to the femur, providing stability. In addition to providing forward and backward protection, the ACL also provides rotational support and stability to the knee during varus or valgus stress.[2]

Unfortunately, ACL injuries are quite common, affecting approximately 100,000 to 200,000 US athletes annually.[3] The ACL is the most commonly injured ligament in the knee. The annual reported incidence in the US alone is roughly one in 3,500 people. Most ACL tears occur in athletes during non-contact situations, similar to my own. There are many risk factors that increase one's chance of ACL injuries, such as previous injury or surgery, poor muscle strength/conditioning, lack of core strength and neuromuscular control (proprioception), and shoe type.[4]

Current research suggests that there is no age or gender bias, although many researchers have claimed that women are at an increased risk of sustaining an ACL injury due to a variety of factors.[5] Some studies suggest that females may have weaker hamstrings and prioritize using the quadriceps muscle group while decelerating. Engaging the quadriceps musculature while slowing down places abnormally increased stress on the ACL, as the quadriceps muscles are less effective at preventing anterior tibial translation than the hamstring muscles.[6,7] With that being said, the risk is apparent to everyone. The National Football League (NFL), arguably home to the most athletic, strong, and naturally gifted athletes on the planet, has seen countless ACL tears for years. In 2020, during preseason practices alone, there were eleven ACL tears. From 2016 to 2020, the average was 10.4 ACL tears during the preseason.[8]

The prevalence of this injury can also be seen globally, not just in the US. The global cruciate ligament repair procedures market size was valued at 8.4 billion USD in 2018 and is expected to register a compound annual growth rate of over 9 percent by 2025. According to the best available data, around 2.5 million knee reconstruction surgeries were performed in 2018, and it is also expected to grow precipitously through 2025.[9]

After seeing all of these numbers, you would think that every facet of ACL rehabilitation has been hashed out, is supremely effective, and foolproof. Right? To that, I ask you one simple question. During your entire time struggling with the trauma, healing, and rehabilitation (whether you just started or have been working with it for months), have you ever felt 100 percent peaceful psychologically? I am willing to wager the answer is "no." If your answer is "yes," consider yourself lucky. Most people do not feel at ease after suffering this injury.

Can you think of any other aspects of sports that are ignored more diligently than your emotional and psychological health? If an athlete struggles with remembering plays, footwork, grades, or issues with the physical component of an injury, numerous solutions are routinely discussed with athletes. Doesn't it seem peculiar that all of these components are addressed in excruciating detail, yet the innermost workings of our psychological and emotional health are left unattended and undervalued?

The psychological trauma of an ACL tear is one that plagues many athletes. Some research suggests that psychological stress contributes to a higher chance of re-injury.[10] As seen in the NFL, where psychological health is becoming increasingly prioritized, this has become a prevalent issue among professional athletes, and it can be life-threatening.

Despite its prevalence, the psychological impacts of an ACL tear are not discussed with patients at length during their time working through rehabilitation. All the physical aspects are examined in detail, yet the psychological effects are too often ignored. Even though psychological stress has been linked to an increased likelihood of re-injury, clinicians would rather avoid discussing the emotional components altogether than discuss them openly. With more research into these elements, ACL rehabilitation training could be advanced to address these topics with patients. ACL tears are a complex phenomenon that cannot be solved by ACL repair alone. To reduce ACL injuries and ensure athlete safety, more attention must be paid to the psychological components of injury management.

Chapter 2: The After

"Human well-being must be at the heart of elite athletic performance. Athletes should feel empowered and nurtured both physically and mentally ... mental health and physical health are two halves of a whole, and care for both must be seen as a priority."

–Abhinav Bindra
Olympic champion and IOC Athletes' Commission Member

The image seared into my brain after that unforgiving "pop" was the look of confusion, followed by sympathy, from my teammate that I was moments before competing against. He and everyone else who witnessed the incident immediately had the exact same thoughts that I did after I hit the ground:

"He tore it."

"Did you hear the pop?"

"Was that what I think it was?"

I gingerly got to my feet and remembered being almost certain nothing was wrong. I felt the same as moments before. There was no excruciating pain that everyone rightly assumed went hand-in-hand with that tell-tale sound.

That all changed when I tried to walk. Although I still had no pain, I felt a little off-balance. I pictured a baby giraffe's first steps or the feeling of carrying one thing on top of another. That movement that you can feel but cannot directly control. Using this new gait, I walked over to the head athletic trainer, who pleasantly asked, "What's up?" He had obviously missed the scene of what appeared to be me getting sniped by an invisible assassin during the one-on-one drill toward the other end of the field. I explained to him what happened, and his face darkened. The more I explained, the more solemn and concerned he looked, which naturally raised my heart rate and concern drastically. At this point, I was still clinging to the thought that it was a fluke. Everything was alright. It was just a tweak. I would take a break and then be able to jump back into the swing of things later in practice, or this afternoon's practice.

He had me sit down and told me to relax my leg. This, as you likely know as well, is nearly impossible as the thoughts of what could be run rampant through your head. This test, called the Lachman's test, would prove to be a big part of not only my next few weeks, but my next few years. If you haven't had the pleasure of someone testing your ACL, I wouldn't recommend it (0/10). The athletic trainer did what all good people would do. He gave me hope, stating, "It feels like everything is in place." This made my heart somersault with joy, but that was short-lived. He then said, "To be sure, we should get you set up with an appointment with the team physician." My mood had bounced from panicked to relaxed to doubly panicked, and I was certainly done riding this emotional rollercoaster.

It was at this time that I shattered. I finally understood the athletes on TV. It's common for people to believe that an ACL rupture is excruciatingly painful. How can it not be? You may watch videos of world-class athletes weeping uncontrollably after suffering an injury. But, if I suffered such an injury, why wasn't I in agony? That response is straightforward.

I was.

It was at that moment that I recalled everything I'd heard about ACL tears. The athletes who were hurt by this condition, the length of time it took to recover, and the chance of them returning to their previous level of performance all came flooding back. It all made me feel like I was going to vomit.

I cried for what I, potentially, had lost. My first love. The sport that got me out of a difficult hometown. The dreams for not only this season but my senior season and beyond. What if I was never the same? Was there anything I could do?

This pain sank deep into me and fused with my very being from that moment to this very day. Since then, 2,239 days have passed since that fateful day, and the thought of those feelings is still difficult for me to overcome. Do you want to know the worst part? As I sat on the football cart, drowning in my own psychological pain, my dying dreams, and lost aspirations, I was alone.

The only way I can describe these thoughts is through the imagery of sinking. Imagine everything you have ever wanted athletically. Every athlete has a snapshot of what that looks like to them. Picture it vividly. Now, imagine the floor of that picture turning into a water-like substance beneath your feet, and you slowly sink. You can still see the image of what you wanted, but your knee serves as an anchor that drags you further and deeper. Even thinking about looking up toward what may have been, what you've always desired, is more painful than looking around in the dark. You make yourself at home in this desperate, lonely place.

My athletic trainer, coach, teammates, friends, and family never advised me to get professional assistance in dealing with the torrent of emotions that poured over me. Why would they? On either end of the spectrum, mental health and sports might appear to be polar opposites. As athletes, we assume asking for help, or needing help, makes us weak. This mindset couldn't be further from the truth. Pope Paul once said, "Nothing makes one feel so strong as a call for help." No one is perfect. To be the best version of yourself, it is logical to get help from others. What is truly illogical is how stigma keeps athletes from receiving the care they require.

The World Health Organization's (WHO) recent data shows that depression was estimated to be the second most common disorder that leads to disability in 2020.[11] In the United States, 46.6 million adults experienced a range of mid to major mental health conditions in 2017, of which over 11 million were categorized as major conditions causing serious functional impairment.[12] Even though mental illness is widespread throughout the globe, stigma continues to be prevalent across various societies and cultures. The WHO defines stigma as "a mark of shame, disgrace, or disapproval that results in an individual being rejected, discriminated against, and excluded from participating in different areas of society."[13] With the growing unease in today's society revolving around mental health, it is understandable that athletes would steer clear of anything that could potentially put them in a compromised position.

Athletes are even more affected by this stigma. For the most part, it has been fed to us since we were children that we are strong and self-reliant and that mental health problems are "for the weak." The first half of that statement is correct. You are physically robust and self-sufficient. However, that does not imply you're invulnerable to suffering or sadness. The stereotype of "just do it" and "what doesn't kill you makes you stronger" is toxic in athletics, and I will be the first to say that I was previously under the same delusion. A recent study showed a strong negative correlation between student athletes' mental health stigma and the likelihood of them seeking psychological help.[14]

Given the culture of collegiate sports, this statistic could be a deadly combination. Your sport is your life as a college athlete. Anyone who has spent any amount of time as a student-athlete will confirm this. You spend an overwhelming majority of your time with your teammates and coaches. If they promote the myth that expressing your sentiments shows a lack of strength, and the outside society places a huge stigma on any mental illness, what's the likelihood you will speak up if you're desperate?

It's okay to not be okay.

If you're feeling anxious, depressed, discouraged, or any other negative emotion regarding your psychological health and this injury … it is OKAY. I cannot emphasize enough how important it is for you to accept where you are in the process of psychological healing and rehabilitation before attempting to change anything else about your psychological health. It is not simple, but it is essential. Everyone's emotional recovery process is unique. The only way to determine where we are in our mental healing is to evaluate ourselves objectively and trust what we feel about our mental health. The more you're able to acknowledge your present state based on your evaluation, the faster your emotional health will improve.

However, you may be thinking, "But I don't have a formal diagnosis; I'm not THAT screwed up!" I understand the sentiment, and you are undoubtedly correct. You may not have a formal diagnosis like me, and you could be further along in your psychological healing than I was. What I'm here to convey is that, in my opinion, we both recognize that this injury and its recovery are not only physical. Addressing the physical aspects of an ACL injury is like emptying a flooded basement while ignoring the out-of-sight leaking pipe that continues to cause damage to your home's foundation.

Simply said, tackling the entire problem rather than just the apparent component (i.e., range of motion, strength, scarring, etc.) is necessary whether you have a flooded basement or a damaged ACL. Typically, as with many other things in life, acceptance is first required before anything else may begin.

Chapter 3: The First Rehabilitation

"Success is not built on success. It's built on failure. It's built on frustration. Sometimes, it's built on catastrophe."

–Sumner Redstone

One thing is always certain for injured athletes, whether you'll admit it or not. There is a release of pressure in not competing, but that lack of competition, of comradery, and many times purpose, turns a short relief into a nightmare. That fact is especially true for anyone who has had an injury that takes an inordinate amount of time to heal, like an ACL tear.

Instead of getting to spend our time doing what we love, we are forced to watch others do it. We are forced to watch others do exactly what we want to do when we physically cannot. That is demoralizing. It is also usually the first look at how truly lacking we are in the skills to combat these feelings of drastically lowered self-esteem, self-identity, and purpose.

One of the first things anyone asks in college or life is: "What do you do?" Or essentially, "Who are you?" As an athlete, I was a football player; as a professional, I am a therapist and a writer. Answering these simple questions when you are hurt is painful because it is a constant reminder that even though that is how you identify, it is not presently true. Our very being is tied to these activities to which we have pledged our time, money, and life.

While your self-identity and self-esteem are destroyed, you are also heavily persuaded to go through surgery, essentially relearn how to walk, and have to rebuild every musculature that is important to athletics in your leg. Many people don't realize this, but after surgery, the muscles involved are "shut off" and are very difficult to turn back on as the athlete starts therapy. One such muscle is the vastus medialis and, more specifically, the vastus medialis oblique (VMO). This muscle is one of the most difficult to return to previous abilities after surgery.

I spent months and months full of treatments, rehabilitation, and testing, following precisely what the athletic trainers, physical therapists, and exercise science professionals deemed appropriate for me to do. While they are all great people and professionals, I never felt the same.

At one point, I could squat more than my pre-injury max. That was probably the most frustrated I got as an athlete. I thought that would be when I was feeling ready to return. I thought that I would be "back" and better than ever. Unfortunately, that was not the case. I still had daily pain and constantly felt like I had gotten a leg transplant. It is rather hard to explain to someone who hasn't had an ACL injury, but things that were previously easy, painless, and second nature became robotic and foreign.

While this book isn't about what I deem the appropriate physical training that needs to be done for these athletes, it is important to know how frustrating and maddening it is to do everything "right" but not ever feel the way you want to again.

This anger continued to grow right up to my senior season. That season I had dreamed of my whole life was all taken from me by a freak accident and a small unfortunate pop in my knee. I felt as ready as I could and had passed all the necessary physical assessments to be cleared for full competition.

Unfortunately, I was never able to compete.

On the day my senior fall camp was starting, I was deemed "ineligible." Not due to poor grades; I had great grades, attendance, etc. It was because I had *too many credits*. I was a transfer student, and my advisors and coaches had neglected to tell me that I didn't need to take a full load of credits the year prior while I went through my rehabilitation and prepared for graduate school.

To say I was mad would drastically downplay how I felt. I had given my body, time, and resources to this endeavor, only to be unable to compete with my teammates and brothers for the last season I had at the school. After I heard the news, I essentially went into a numb coma. I am sure that is not the best way to convey the situation, but it is how I felt, and I remember the entire aftermath vividly. I felt I truly had no purpose in my life anymore, and everything I had worked for was all for *nothing*. I was in my apartment on campus for days on end and skipped numerous practices, meetings, etc. Eventually, my coach reached out to explain I still had an obligation to be part of the team and attend meetings, practices, games, etc. I found this very … difficult to stomach. To be lectured about obligation by someone who had failed in his obligations to me felt like salt in my new wound. I begrudgingly agreed because of my love for my teammates.

That year was the beginning of the end of my somewhat-balanced mental health. While I *thought* I knew anxiety and depression before, this period of my life opened all sorts of dark new doors. I began starving myself, not for any particular purpose other than it was something I could control. Anyone who has anxiety knows that the things you can control are the things you are most likely to abuse. I completely turned toward my physique during this time, and I took out all of my frustration on it. I started "intermittent fasting," or, essentially, a perennial excuse for why no one would see me eat—followed by periods of binging, which naturally made me hate myself even more. So, the cycle would continue.

After a couple of months of this self-destruction, I found some internal clarity. I looked to my inner child and decided I would listen to him. I knew that I had always yearned to play sports after college, like many others, but had mainly focused on the present challenge of college football. It was at this point, in the late hours of the evening, that I started searching for a way to make it to the next opportunity of my career. I Googled "best training facilities in my area" and connected to trainers to help me begin training for professional tryouts.

Chapter 4: The Second Tear

"Hardships often prepare ordinary people for an extraordinary destiny."

–C.S. Lewis.

I was progressing. I trained incessantly at a sport-based training facility in the area multiple times weekly while ramping up my weight-lifting regimen. I had found a new focus, a new hope. This newfound invigoration for life was helpful, but it did not overcome the pain I had recently endured. My team had finished the season, and I had missed my last opportunity to play with my teammates, some of whom I cared for very much. That reminder, and sting, carried throughout my life and brought cynicism and numbness to me as a person. While I was progressing physically, I was taking large bounds backward in my personal development.

I lost friends and a girlfriend during this time, specifically due to how closed off I was. I was searching to reignite my feelings in any way possible. I would argue and cause intentional emotional pain to others because of how jaded I had become due to the loss and continual hurt I felt when I was on campus or talking to those who got to compete on the team.

As I graduated and went on with my life, I continued to train and almost felt sure of myself. While my training regimen was still not the one I would currently recommend, it had been closer to what gave me hope. I had continued to break strength barriers that I hadn't reached before, all while continuing to struggle with my nutrition, interpersonal relationships, and self-esteem. This period, while still bleak, provided me with a few memories that I hold very dear. It was during this time I had the opportunity to sign my agent, who gave me the opportunity to train in Long Beach, California, with NFL trainers and other athletes who were training for combines as well. That opportunity was a big moment for me to notice where I truly was, and I am thankful for it to this very day.

After my training had peaked, I was invited to a private Canadian Football League (CFL) workout in Ohio, where a number of teams would evaluate my physical attributes and have me complete several drills.

Everything had gone well. I didn't get all the marks I was hoping for, but I was still happy with my overall performance. Having not competed for a year and a couple of months, I was tired by the end of the 2.5-hour session. However, I had done well in all of my 1:1s and just needed one more rep until I was done for the day.

This rep was against a player from West Virginia University, and the offensive lineman had been phenomenal all day. I had been looking forward to going against him and seeing how I truly stacked up against a player from a much larger school. My anxiety soared as we lined up and as the rep started. Due to all the pent-up energy, I had a good get-off and was able to reach his shoulder and deflect his first hand from touching me. I just had to do one more thing to win the rep: pivot my body sideways so that I could slip past him. I leaned into the pivot, opening my hips to put my right leg out front (the same movement I had torn my left ACL on previously, except reversed), and suddenly fell without warning.

The pop was audible.

The closest coach immediately came and helped me up and told me he appreciated me being there. He knew precisely what had just happened, and so did I.

I had just lost my last opportunity and had played my last snap as a football player.

It was the end of my career and the beginning of the end of my fluctuating mental health. The downturn was quick and steep.

Chapter 5: Background

"Soak up the views. Take in the bad weather and the good weather. You are not the storm."

–Matt Haig

Note: This chapter contains sensitive material relating to substance abuse and suicidal ideation. Proceed at your discretion.

Athletes are amazing. The physical feats that athletes continually produce marvel the rest of the world. Whether it is Usain Bolt running a 9.58-second 100-meter dash, Jesse Owens breaking three world records in one hour, or Kobe Bryant scoring 81 points in a single game, one thing is certain—the world looks up to athletes; they are our heroes. The problem with heroes is that they are aware they are the heroes of many. Think of someone that looks up to you. A family friend, neighbor kid, or your own sibling could be the culprit. Do they know everything "wrong" with you? Humans are imperfect by nature. That is a reality. But do you want people to know about your flaws, difficulties, and challenges? I'm guessing most would say "no."

We, as athletes, have been taught to be resilient at all costs. It is ingrained in the athletic culture, and, in many cases, it is quite harmful to an athlete's mental well-being. This poisonous culture makes it even less likely for a participant to disclose issues psychologically or emotionally. All athletes have scoffed while listening to coaches propose mental visualization exercises or visual imagery at one point or another. I was just like the others until I couldn't afford to be anymore.

I have had difficulties in my life, the same as anyone else might have had. I have suffered loss, family financial struggles, and two ACL injuries. These were all awful at the time and difficult for me to work through. They are what made me interested in psychology and the inner workings of the human brain and our emotions. While I was interested, I never truly studied or utilized therapy or different mental health skills that could positively impact my life, academics, and athletic career at the time. The reason I didn't is that I didn't *have* to. A series of poor personal choices led me to the trauma that would consume me, giving me no choice but to learn the skills I outline in this book.

Vibrations in my pocket alerted me to the time. It was now 8:00 p.m., which meant it had been roughly two hours since she had been passed out in the bathroom. She was due to wake up in fifteen to thirty minutes, so it was best for me to put her son to bed before she woke up. I closed my computer and hoped I had spent enough time studying for my exam in the morning. He fell asleep without much issue and just in time as well. She woke up more aggressive than usual tonight, which was unfortunate. She stumbled from our bathroom, which still stunk of puke, bile, and vodka, and asked where her son was. I informed her that he was asleep. She grumbled and went to her purse. I hated that purse, and truly all purses. To this day, they remind me of the 99 vodka shots. After she found more of the ever-multiplying shots from her purse, she came and sat next to me. This particular night, she held the bottles up in front of my face. "Just drink them. You know I will if you don't," she said, "then I will be sick again for a couple of days." Knowing full well I had to complete her homework, wash the bathroom, and clean the kitchen already, I offered to pour them down the drain. This was too straightforward, and it never worked out as well as I hoped. She answered, "I will kill myself if I drink any more tonight."

As much as I hate to admit it, those words felt typical at this point in my life. I sat quietly and didn't respond, calculating the best way to handle the oncoming situation. A game that I was all too used to playing. I decided to protect her and agreed to take the shots. It was only six tonight, but after being gone at school all day, I had no idea how much she had consumed earlier. Judging by the amount of cleaning necessary in our master bathroom, it was much more than six. After finishing the shots, I felt the usual warmth but also the usual regret. I had not spent an entire day sober in months. For whatever reason, I didn't get hungover, which was likely the only way I had been able to pass my doctoral classes at the time. When she got her way, she had the tendency to push the envelope. This would be one of those times.

She went over to the counter and got out the apple cider vinegar. She claimed to use it for weight loss and overall health. Looking back, it was nearly comical as she spent most of her waking hours puking, but that's beside the point. She poured two 6-ounce glasses of them and brought them over to the couch with a smile on her face. Feeling drunk and stressed, I told her I couldn't and reminded her how badly it messed with my anxiety medication. Drinking apple cider vinegar, for whatever reason, felt like drinking 10+ shots when mixed with the anxiety medications I was taking. Sometimes, I couldn't even walk. She usually threatened to harm herself until I drank it with her. Knowing I couldn't let her child see her harmed or dead in the morning, I wrongly obliged and gave ground.

Afterward, I sat in the living room, and the world truly felt like it was spinning in every direction imaginable. She laughed and claimed I was lying, per usual. Then, when she wanted to "go on a drive," likely to get more of the substance ruining our life, I refused. Partly because I could hardly walk, and partly because I detested leaving her son alone at night. Seeing that I was unable to come, she took that as her usual chance to go get more alcohol. When she got back twenty minutes later with what I assumed was copious amounts of alcohol … I was upset. I still could hardly move, but the world had stopped spinning so rapidly. She seemed to notice that I was growing tired of this game. She took a shot and grabbed the butcher knife.

I asked her why she continued to inflict this on herself, me, and her child. I informed her that I knew she had the power to stop, achieve good grades, and be the person she desired to be. She took it as a slap in the face, held a knife against my neck, and said, "Why don't you just date one of the girls in your stupid class? Oh yeah, I remember. You can't! No one would want someone who is so screwed up with anxiety." It was at this point that I had the first of many suicidal thoughts. It got to the point where I would wish she would act on her threats to my physical well-being.

While these may not be the reasons you are pursuing help, I applaud you. I required much more to be prompted to find the skills necessary for healing. Those were the situations that forced me to find help and led me to Acceptance and Commitment Therapy (ACT).

Before discussing ACT (pronounced "act"), I think it is important to go over the framework in which it is embedded. The framework associated with ACT is the Relational Frame Theory (RFT), which is a theory that analyzes both cognition and language. Research led by Dr. Steven Hayes, in collaboration with Dermot Barnes-Holmes, has helped bring this theory to the forefront of psychology in an attempt to complete or "fill in" the gaps left by B.F Skinner. Skinner provided fantastic research, but he lacked the ability to adequately describe language and how individuals communicate. The basic tenets of RFT can be distilled into the following crude example:

> *There are relations that, as young humans, we are taught, such as "green means go" when driving. It is safe to say those unspoken relationships are inferred based on that lesson (go is related to the color green while driving).*

Coming to the second conclusion may be simple, but it took us quite a bit of practice to become sufficient.[15]

Other non-verbal animals are unable to perform this skill; it allows us to produce sounds that we, as humans, can relate to the objects in which others understand. Naming objects is just one example of RFT.[16]

Many other examples can be provided, such as one that can be found on contextualscience.org. The one I relate to the most is an example by Dr. Hayes that states:[17]

Let's say you and I bump into each other at a local grocery store, and I introduce you to my brother, Phil, and my father, Greg. Although I've only given you two pieces of information:

- Phil is my brother.
- Greg is my father.

From those two facts, you can derive four additional relationships without explicitly being told:

- I am Phil's brother.
- I am Greg's son.
- Phil is Greg's son.
- Greg is Phil's father.

That is SIX relationships from just two pieces of information. This can obviously continue to compound by giving you additional information like:

- Stacy is my mother.
- Josephine is my niece.

Combining that information with the previously known information will give you a slough of additional relationships, which can continue to compound. At this point, it is pertinent to note that assumptions will be involved to some degree. Obviously, there are additional relations that you routinely analyze, such as:

- Different and same.
- Mine and yours.
- Here and there.
- Slower and faster.
- Later and earlier.
- Further and closer.
- Different and same.

While other animals may be able to do this, it is a uniquely human ability to determine relationships that are not obvious. For example, symbolic comparisons posit that a dime has a higher value than a nickel, even though it appears to be counterintuitive. Additionally, we all call a bound collection of words on paper a "book" because we all agree on the naming convention. These symbols are obviously arbitrary but hugely beneficial and efficient. We can also attach emotions to memories, thoughts, and symbols, which work in the same bi-directional capacity as discussed regarding the "green light."

An example of this could be you taking your dog to the veterinarian to get shots. The dog ended up hating the shots, and forevermore will associate needles and the veterinarian with the pain he felt on that day. The next time he sees a needle, he may struggle to flee, bark, etc. Due to his memory of pain in the past, he will try to flee prior to feeling it again. Research has shown that animals can be trained to signal whether they have experienced a painful event; when they do so, though, there are no signs of distress. Even though they remember pain, they are calm. On the other hand, we, as humans, will show signs of distress when describing a previous painful experience. It is quite possible to endure more pain when reliving a past traumatic experience than when the event itself happened. If we are careless, we can attach other words to the painful event.

For example, we could replace the word "needle" with something that has a positive connotation, like "apple pie." If you dislike shots and try to distract yourself by repeatedly thinking about "apple pie," it may work initially. But eventually, that approach will likely backfire because while you are thinking about apple pie, you will eventually associate apple pie with shots or needles. This is an example of how strategies to avoid pain can create additional things that can serve as reminders of the pain we are trying to avoid.[18]

ACT is different from more well-known treatments, such as Cognitive Behavioral Therapy (CBT). The architecture by which ACT works, as you may remember, is RFT.

Simply stated, ACT teaches people how to engage and overcome difficult or painful feelings, experiences, and thoughts through acceptance and mindfulness techniques. These techniques develop self-compassion, psychological flexibility, and the ability to build life-enhancing patterns of behavior. ACT is not about overcoming or battling difficult emotions or pain; it is about learning to live with those difficult feelings. This technique offers a way to let go of your suffering by living a life based on what matters most to you.

ACT has been developed through scientific exploration, and there has been and continues to be, an extensive research community that analyzes the science within ACT and its efficacy when treating a wide array of different psychological problems, such as:

- Depression
- Anxiety
- PTSD
- Substance abuse
- Psychosis

- Pain
- Eating disorders
- Weight management

ACT includes six individual pivots (explained soon) that can assist you in your journey of living with the psychological pain and dysfunction your ACL injury has caused you more effectively. The first pivot is understanding the difference between yourself and your pessimist. Prior to delving deeper into ACT, it is important to understand what differentiates it from previous methods.

Chapter 6: The Difference Between ACT and CBT

"Happiness is not a destination. It is a method of life."

–Burton Hill

First, it is pertinent to describe the elements of Acceptance and Commitment Therapy (ACT) and compare it to more "well-known" interventions, like Cognitive-Behavioral Therapy (CBT).

CBT aims to help clients reduce their distress by changing their cognitive and behavioral responses to anxiety or any distressful situation.[19,20] From the learning theory perspective, CBT enables clients to develop a new, associative network of adaptive thoughts and behaviors that compete with or modify maladaptive, fear-based networks and memories.[21] Toward that aim, CBT for anxiety disorders (as an example) may include the following components:[22]

(a) psychoeducation on the nature of fear/anxiety

(b) self-monitoring of symptoms

(c) relaxation/breathing retraining

(d) cognitive restructuring (logical empiricism and disconfirmation)

(e) behavioral experiments

(f) imaginal and in vivo exposure to feared images, bodily sensations, and situations

(g) weaning of safety signals

(h) response and relapse prevention.

In cognitive restructuring, clients learn to challenge anxious thoughts. They can think of reasons why the thought might not be true. In behavioral experiments, the participants approach the stressor and then see whether a negative response occurs. Response prevention attempts to expose clients to stressors and contexts while preventing anxiety-reducing and avoidant behaviors. More streamlined CBT therapy may include only psychoeducation, cognitive restructuring, and behavioral exposure.[23]

Now, before you get too worried, I understand this may seem like a lot. I want you to know that, essentially, CBT wants to challenge your negative thoughts. CBT's main aim is to reduce your symptoms. Personally, I have always struggled with their framework because I am the type of person who, when told "don't look over there," proceeds to look precisely in the direction I am told not to. The same can be said for thoughts. If I "challenge" every thought, I notice that my thoughts are supremely resilient and tend to come back no matter how hard I try to push them away.

On the other hand, ACT is a behavioral therapy that uses six distinct pivots that work collaboratively to form a cohesive unit. This unit allows you to go through life with the skills necessary in order to face the inevitable challenges we all will face. The six pivots of ACT are:[24]

1. Cognitive Defusion
2. Self as Context
3. Acceptance
4. Mindfulness
5. Personal Values
6. Committed Action

Within ACT, psychological flexibility is defined as enhancing the capacity of clients to make contact with their experience in the present moment and, based on what is possible for them at that moment, choose to act in ways that are consistent with their chosen values.[25] From a broader perspective, ACT is grounded in radical behaviorism and attempts to integrate cognition and language into a behavioral analytic framework. The components, or pivots, of ACT will be explored in more detail later in this book.

ACT describes itself as based on an extensive empirical, theoretical, and philosophical research program that demonstrates how language embroils clients in a fight with themselves and their experience.[26] This research program centers on the relational frame theory (RFT), a "post-Skinnerian" contextual behavioral theory about how language influences cognition, emotion, and behavior.[27,28]

From the perspective of RFT, "the core of human language and cognition is the learned and contextually controlled ability to arbitrarily relate events mutually and in combination, and to change the functions of specific events based on their relations to others."[29] This seems highly technical, but it can be simplified. For instance, the harder you fight not to have your anxiety, depression, and trauma control your life, the more it does. Your mind does this by relating seemingly unrelated items.

For example, imagine every time you got upset, you were told to think of your favorite ice cream. No matter how adamantly you wanted to think about your favorite ice cream, the unwanted thoughts would return. Eventually, your favorite ice cream will also be associated with unwanted thoughts, creating less room in your life for the activities or things you love.

Consequently, previously unassociated thoughts, actions, and words of the real world can become fused with our stressor and form symbolic relationships, growing the number of negative stimuli that could cause adverse reactions or psychological distress.[30] For example, after I tore my ACL, I could no longer participate in intramurals. Even when I felt strong enough to do so, I was scared. This was because, for so long, I had to turn down my friends and classmates who would ask me to play. Even when I *could* play, I would get anxious, and my first reaction was to avoid those situations. Now that I have grown with the help of ACT, I have been able to take my life back into my own hands and do what I love.

Like CBT, ACT involves the development of an objective stance toward one's thoughts, feelings, and behaviors. However, it does not subsequently target them for logical disconfirmation, change, and control. Rather, self-observance is framed within the perspective of mindfulness: to live as fully as possible in the present moment, with acceptance toward whatever one is experiencing,[31] be it "good, bad, or ugly."[32] Thus, the goal is not changing cognitions or symptoms, as in CBT, but mindful tolerance and acceptance of cognitions and symptoms. Within ACT, behavior alone is targeted for content change. Beyond cognitive defusion, additional components of ACT treatment for anxiety disorders include psychoeducation, creative hopelessness, life values work, value-guided exposure, and behavioral willingness/committed action.[33]

On the surface, ACT and CBT for ACL patients are quite different in both the procedures and goals of therapy. Hence, we begin by offering critical reflections on the major differences that pervade the research and clinical dialogue on ACT and CBT, including cognitive restructuring versus cognitive defusion (and acceptance), prediction and control versus acceptance, and anxiety symptoms versus life goals.[34]

From the perspective of ACT, CBT focuses too greatly on the content of cognition, thereby keeping the ruminative cycle alive.[35,36] According to the ACT model, countering anxious thoughts with judging and modifying thought content may intensify the struggle to rid oneself of anxious thinking. Picture someone yelling, "Don't look!" From my viewpoint, as stated previously, it is almost impossible not to look. This is the same view that ACT and its framework hold. ACT-based acceptance and cognitive defusion are proposed as a means of sidestepping the ruminative trap of cognition and accessing experience directly.[37]

Both ACT and CBT coping methods with anxious or depressive cognition require additional thinking so as not to get tied up in your thoughts. This additional thinking takes the form of self-talk or coaching. Even when quietly meditating, self-talk in the form of verbal coaching is readily present. It may be argued that some forms of self-talk, coaching, and thinking are better than others. For example, ACT wisely bypasses "fighting" about which side of a thought has greater evidence by viewing such fights from the perspective of a meta-cognitive understanding of what minds do (i.e., that minds often produce anxious and contradictory thoughts and that this is normal).[38] Put simply, ACT takes the whole thought into consideration and allows you to notice and utilize or disregard thoughts, based on which thoughts will assist you in moving toward your values.

Cognitive restructuring in CBT and cognitive defusion in ACT both aim to reduce avoidance and enhance exposure to previously avoided and suppressed internal experiences. An example, for me personally, is resuming normal athletic activity after my surgeries. Cognitive restructuring would posit that I would be best served to challenge the thoughts that I may get reinjured. Cognitive defusion would posit that although I have thoughts of getting re-injured, that doesn't necessarily mean I will get reinjured. I also have thoughts like:

"What if my car didn't start?"

"Why aren't there any more animals that hibernate?"

"If I time traveled, I would totally catch an MJ-led Bulls' game."

That is the thing about thoughts; we can't control them. They are subconscious, and there is no use wrestling with something we cannot change.

Therefore, both may serve to reduce "experiential avoidance," the term used in ACT to describe the avoidance of uncomfortable internal thoughts, sensations, and feelings.[39] A direct comparison of these two strategies for coping with negative thoughts is needed to investigate this claim empirically and to determine if these strategies produce differences in emotional coping, behavioral approach/avoidance, or physiology.[40]

Prediction and control (CBT) versus acceptance (ACT) of anxiety arises as a major potential difference between CBT and ACT therapeutic approaches. CBT has been criticized because its goals of symptom prediction, especially symptom control and immediate fear reduction, are impossible to achieve and even counterproductive for most clinical problems.[41] The alternative approach proposed by ACT is acceptance of symptoms (and control of behavior). Acceptance within ACT is defined as "an active taking in of an event or situation … [an] abandonment of dysfunctional [symptom] change agendas and an active process of feeling feelings as feelings, thinking thoughts as thoughts … and so on." [42]

One of the major ways in which ACT and CBT presumably differ is that ACT aims for valued living (via values-driven behavior), whereas CBT aims for symptom reduction as the outcome of therapy.[43,44] ACT is commendable for directly discussing the important factor of values with clients. Values-based and anxiety-reduction goals, however, may not be mutually exclusive. It seems unlikely that CBT therapists aim to reduce negative symptomology so that their clients can do nothing all day. CBT does not emphasize valued living as explicitly as ACT and generally endorses that achieving life goals is easier in the context of having less anxiety. However, facilitating a fulfilling life may be central to both. Furthermore, there is no evidence that promoting anxiety symptom reduction in CBT versus valued living in ACT results in different therapy outcomes.[45]

The difference between ACT and CBT is how directly valued living versus symptom reduction are addressed in therapy and the directionality of their relationship. In ACT, valued living is addressed directly via creative exercises and explicit discussion; in CBT, it is raised implicitly in the creation and enactment of client-driven exposure hierarchies.

In ACT, the emphasis on values-driven behavior may lead to behavioral exposures and, hence, to eventual anxiety reduction. Anxiety reduction that stems from valued living likely reinforces valued living. In CBT, behavioral exposure to feared situations, which likely represent personally valued behaviors, leads to anxiety reduction; in turn, this results in a greater likelihood of engagement in previously avoided, valued behaviors. Exposure may also lead to a greater sense of self-efficacy, mastery, and control, which leads to greater confidence in one's capacity to work toward life goals and values.[46]

Despite the differences between CBT and ACT, both therapies appear to be effective in reducing anxiety symptoms and improving quality of life. The key difference seems to be that CBT focuses on symptom reduction as the primary goal, while ACT aims for valued living through six specific pivots. However, it is important to note that these goals are not mutually exclusive and that both therapies encourage their clients to work toward life enrichment and personal fulfillment.

Chapter 7: Defusion

"To realize that you are not your thoughts is when you begin to awaken spiritually."

–Eckhart Tolle

Have you ever met someone who was almost annoyingly optimistic?

That has always been, and will forever be, me. Throughout my life, I have found that no matter the situation, I can turn nearly any negative into a positive. For example, the previous ACL surgeries and trauma I endured altered the trajectory of my life, and they, daresay, expedited my psychological growth out of necessity. Think of celebrity comedians. They appear happy, positive, and inherently "carefree," but that is far from the truth. There is a slew of legendary comedians who have taken their lives or come out and publicized their mental health issues.

The lesson we can all learn from this is that outward appearances do not tell the whole story. We all have irrational worrying, negative thoughts, or feelings. I have learned to alleviate the effects of these worries, negative thoughts, or feelings through my own ACT therapy and by continually sharpening certain skills.

It was 12:48 p.m. Most of my classmates were enjoying lunch, socializing, and taking full advantage of the lunch hour. Unfortunately, I was not able to do so. I was confined to a bathroom stall more and more often. It was my only respite from the social pressures that always seemed to be stoking the fires of my newly diagnosed anxiety. Many athletes are perfectionists, not necessarily by choice but out of ambition.

My mother and father were both basketball coaches. I spent my entire childhood dribbling and shooting a basketball at both their team's practices and my own practices. I loved basketball growing up. It connected my father and me in ways I will never truly understand. My father was very passionate about basketball, which was always very apparent to me. One of the first memories I can remember is when I was around three years old. I remember sitting on our porch watching my dad shoot baskets for hours across the street in a church parking lot. That moment has always been frozen in my mind, and I drew on it plenty growing up. Like my father, I spent countless hours shooting baskets, using it as my own personal therapy. The repetition, sounds, and exercise gave me peace. That peace turned into a dream.

My father was one of the first athletes from my hometown to play a Division I sport. Most of the population of my hometown, like many small towns, never left. I had an aversion to that idea and knew I needed a way out. So, I channeled what used to be therapeutic and turned it into a mountainous goal. While it initially gave me even more drive to excel and hone my physical attributes, like speed, coordination, etc., it would soon give me much more than I bargained for. The years passed, and I had a decent amount of success through elementary and middle school. Then, I started high school. The culmination of all of my work would truly be put on display. While I made the JV team and started (which wasn't altogether common at that time) as a freshman, I was not pleased. I continued to work hard and eventually was brought up as a "floater," which meant I was able to warm up and essentially be present for varsity games at the end of the season. While this was a huge success (at the time) for me, I would later look at it as one of the worst things that had ever happened to me.

I took that supposed "win" as myself stepping over the threshold to what I had always wanted. At the end of that season and freshman year overall, I had been successful in football (especially), basketball, and somewhat in track.

During the summer after my freshman year, I learned that I had broken both pedicles of my L4 vertebrae. The cause was not directly known, but it was thought to be an injury due to repetitive stress on my back from football, basketball, and jumping during track. I would not be able to play football and may not be able to play basketball the following year. Because I had already asserted myself as an up-and-coming athlete to watch in the school, though, I didn't worry initially. That is until I had to watch the *entire* football season.

When you have to watch someone play your sport, in your spot, for the first time, it is very difficult, as you may know. That football season really changed me mentally. I had spent so much time working on myself physically that I never truly spent the time to strengthen myself psychologically, a sentiment I am sure many of you can also agree with. Between being sidelined all season and my previous "successes," the pressure (I felt) was mounting on me to come back and truly show what my teams were missing.

That fall is when I first met my pessimist, or as Dr. Steven Hayes calls it, "the dictator within." This is the voice we all have in our head that speaks negativity into our lives. I listened to the dictator say numerous untrue and unhelpful things over those months, such as: "If you weren't so weak, you'd be playing right now," "You wouldn't have made that tackle," "The coaches have already forgotten about you," etc.

By the time I was cleared to play, the weight of my dictator was almost unbearable. I again floated in basketball after missing football season entirely. This was a huge blow. I remember being so tired BEFORE practice. I would sweat and spend all day worrying about my performance in practice so much that I could hardly compete when I got there. My legs felt like lead, and my chest felt like it had a tight belt compressing my lungs all day.

It was those feelings that led me to the avoidant behavior I spoke of previously. It is how the "successful athlete" ended up taking numerous bathroom breaks for long periods of time, not for digestive issues, but for a much-needed respite from the social pressure I had put myself under. My pessimist or "dictator within" had ruined my life. From the initial injury to this day, this voice inside my head was also present throughout my rehabilitation process during both ACL tears. I routinely deal with combating avoidant behavior for fear of re-injury.

ACT uniquely allows us to let go of the concept of "negative thoughts." Negative thoughts are a concept drawn from traditional CBT. In ACT, every thought should be viewed from a workable or non-workable lens instead of a positive or negative one. This means that even though a thought may be perceived as negative, it could be very useful.

These non-workable thoughts, which I outlined in my previous experiences, are not rare. Literature has shown that as many as 80-99 percent of the population experiences non-workable (or perceived negative) thoughts.[47] These thoughts are associated with a variety of consequences, including negative mood, decreased task performance, and the development of psychopathology.[48] Cognitive fusion occurs when people over-identify with their thoughts, leading to strong emotional responses and a narrowed behavioral repertoire. According to research, cognitive fusion is a risk factor for psychological distress.[49]

So how can someone like me, with cognitive fusion, compounding anxiety, and avoidant behaviors, take the initial step toward living a more productive life? This is where the first pivot, depicted more fully in Dr. Steven

Hayes's *A Liberated Mind*, can be utilized. The literal definition of a pivot is the central point, pin, or shaft on which a mechanism turns or oscillates. This is applicable to injured athletes' lives, as well. We can utilize our momentum or current "action" that hasn't improved our present situation and pivot that energy into a mechanism, backed by scientific evidence, that will help our life "oscillate" or unfold more smoothly. These pivots are minor alterations in how we view, approach, and understand our daily situations or thoughts that can greatly enhance our psychological flexibility and life. The first such pivot is defusion.

Defusion is the skill by which (if routinely practiced) we can distance ourselves from the negative thoughts that wander in and out of our minds throughout the day. The main point that must be reiterated about this skill is that it does not eliminate those negative thoughts or feelings but rather puts our minds on a leash.[50] Cognitive defusion involves undercutting the negative outcomes of thinking by teaching ourselves to get some distance from thoughts by altering our verbal context. For example, defusion is experienced as "having" thoughts and feelings rather than "being" thoughts and feelings.[51]

Defusion has been examined in numerous studies that demonstrate its efficacy.[52,53,54,55,56] Not only does this pivot assist you in minimizing the magnitude and effect of negative thoughts, but it has also displayed positive results in athletic performance. Numerous articles have shown that defusion has had a greater impact than psychological skills training in sport-specific mindfulness skills and training performance.[57,58,59]

Simply stated, there are stacks of literature showing that not only is defusion effective in making these negative thoughts less problematic to you, but it has also been shown to raise athletic performance. That is something that I, like many other injured athletes, could perfect and hone throughout the rehabilitation process. This skill alone could elevate your performance when you are able to return to the field of play.

Most defusion techniques are intended to make the distraction of psychological distress more "top-of-mind" to increase awareness of one's own thought processes.[60] Having a solid understanding of our thought processes allows us to digest things that happen in our minds. All thoughts are not "under control." Realizing that and being able to mindfully let those thoughts drift by will only make you a calmer and more effective athlete (and person). Also, defusion has been highly effective in reducing anxiety and other negative emotions that lead to decreased task performance.[61] This research adequately displays that the more effective you are at reducing the effects of negative emotions on yourself, the more effective you will be at all of your daily tasks, such as athletics.

Improving attention and awareness skills on current-moment experiences may be the key to gaining a greater understanding of behavioral, cognitive, and emotional patterns to which athletes can apply acceptance skills. As a result, athletes who cultivate both attention and acceptance improve their mental and emotional processes over time.[62,63] The combination of boosts in attention/awareness and acceptance may bring about long-term benefits in adaptive behavior that,[64] in turn, may be particularly important for athletes who are expected to perform optimally, sometimes under very challenging and stressful conditions.[65]

Improved sustained attention capabilities during training and competition may make it simpler for athletes to focus on present-tense stimuli, making them less susceptible to various distractions that can hinder high-level performance.[66,67] Also, enhanced attention abilities may increase athletes' capacities to read the game and seize offensive and defensive opportunities. For example, in team sports (e.g., floorball, soccer, ice hockey), a rapid change in circumstances might produce unforeseen gaps and breakthroughs, which may provide scoring opportunities that a less attentive mind may overlook.

Similarly, an enhanced overall self-awareness, combined with greater acceptance of mental and emotional content, can lead to greater attention on the pertinent task at hand, as well as promote self-regulated values-oriented actions while decreasing avoidance and safety behaviors.[68]

Overall, greater attentional capacities may result in athletes' improved abilities to attend to their own current mental processes while simultaneously focusing on athletic performance. This may lead to better on-the-spot decision-making, which could ultimately boost athletes' chances of successful performance.[69] Lastly, attentional self-care is vital for resilience over time, as well as the ability to succeed in high-level performance settings. Thus, mindfulness training enhances attention by cultivating the ability to focus on the present moment.

We can all think of a time when, in athletics, attention to detail was paramount to our success. ACT allows us to practice this skill and be able to rely on it for later athletic or personal situations. In life and sports, giving yourself an advantage is always preferred. Using this skill allowed me to minimize my pre-snap anxiety and truly focus on the movements and reading the offense. I was able to note slight changes that my anxious mind would never have seen. These small skills allowed me to, quite literally, slow the game down.

Presented with valid evidence and numerous benefits of defusion, you may be starting to think that this skill is part of a highly sophisticated type of therapy. Further, this therapy will need to take place at a certain location and time, making it difficult to start seeing the benefits. Those were the same thoughts I had when hearing about these techniques as well. What if I told you that you could do this while you are watching a practice, icing in the athletic training room, or during commercials while watching TV in the evening?

You can.

It is my belief that all ACL patients should utilize defusion practices to enhance the quality of their rehabilitation. As we all know, the process and recovery from an ACL injury is difficult, long, and often frustrating. Utilizing defusion can provide the mind a break from feeling as though it has to be "on" constantly. In other words, these practices can enhance our minds' ability to relax, slow down, and focus on what the next meaningful step is in our recovery.

I still complete defusion exercises nightly during commercials while watching a sporting event, TV show, or the news. It is simple, and better yet, NO ONE has to know you are doing it except you. With the stigma surrounding mental health, this is a huge benefit to beginning your ACT journey. Much like many important journeys in life, it can start with small but meaningful steps.

By detaching from the "pessimist," we are able to truly (maybe for the first time in years) take a look at ourselves. This new perspective is the next pivot and skill that needs to be heightened to take the next small step toward psychological flexibility.

Chapter 8: Self-Pivot

"Until you value yourself, you won't value your time. Until you value your time, you will not do anything with it."

–M. Scott Peck

Imagine a total stranger walking up to you and randomly asking, "Have you ever lied to someone you love?" While this seems awkward and unlikely, give it a real thought. How would you respond?

If you are anything like me, you would offhandedly say, "Of course not!" without giving it a second thought. Have you ever caught yourself lying in daily conversation for no apparent reason? Do you wonder why you did that?

Bella DePaulo, a psychologist at the University of Virginia, completed one of the first studies investigating lies. She and her colleagues investigated nearly 150 people, having the participants take note of their lies in a diary over the course of the week, no matter how small. This research found that most participants lied multiple times daily, including one in five of their social exchanges, and 30 percent of the interactions were one-to-one.[70] Additionally, research found that the type of relationship between parties can have a significant effect on the rate of deception. For example, college students lie to their mothers in half of the conversations that occurred.[71]

While these insignificant lies may not seem substantial or even worth noting, they certainly are part of an overarching flaw in society. These small deceptions strengthen the embodiment of your conceptualized self and diminish your transcendent self. I will explain these concepts later in this chapter.

Trading shoulder pads for crutches and helmets for ice bags is never a situation any athlete wants to be in. Surgery had been around two weeks ago, but it had already felt like a lifetime. How many times can one repeat the same responses?

"I feel better all the time."

"Rehab is going well."

"I'll be stronger than ever."

"I feel stronger today."

"No, that doesn't hurt."

Whenever a teammate, coach, athletic trainer, or therapist worked with me, it was always the same. They would ask the same revolving questions, and I would give them the answers I thought they wanted. Although they were not correct, they were the answers I believed showed me in the best light. I was numb during this period of my life, just like many others. The world continued to rotate around me, but I was frozen in time. I was trapped in a period of my life when not just my body, but also my spirit had been broken. Years after, I can still recall and view those events through the lenses of my eyes and viewpoint.

Think back to a vivid memory you have revolving around the ACL recovery process, whether it is related to physical therapy, interactions with teammates, etc. Just pick a clear memory that you can see through your own eyes as you re-experience that event.

This process has allowed you to observe the sense of "you."

Now, think back to the earliest memory you can conjure from your past. Reach back as far as you can into your childhood, at the most prominent memory you have. Then, relive that event through your current eyes.

Dr. Hayes so eloquently notes in his book, "From that point on, a sense of observing from within our mind from the perspective of an 'I' is a constant in our lives. This 'I' that we become aware of is the 'transcendent self' because it is always there within us, no matter where we are." [72]

Once we have this awareness of "I," we immediately begin developing "self-stories," which give birth to our conceptualized self. The development of these stories can become so entrenched in our minds that we may even conceal who we are from others and, more importantly, ourselves.

To distill this idea down, our "transcendent self" is our true self. Our transcendent self is the truth behind the little white lies. Our conceptualized self is the mask of little lies we tell about ourselves to ensure others see us in the way we deem fit.

Think about a time when you told a small lie. Maybe you said you squatted 400 instead of 365? Maybe you lied about how long it has been since ACL surgery to give the appearance of healing quickly. Maybe you slightly exaggerated your success in a particular game in high school or college. Have you ever told a small lie such as this and then wondered why you even did it? I certainly have. Before engaging in consistent ACT, I noticed myself continually trying to enhance the image of myself I was portraying to others instead of just being myself.

According to the theory, these little deceptions are done in order to feel part of something. As a result, research reveals that the pleasure of others is not beneficial for your self-esteem. In fact, one study revealed that the happiness of others was negatively linked with self-esteem among 230 participants.[73] Another study analyzing 113 participants found that lower self-esteem scores were significantly correlated with higher levels of externality.[74] The main takeaway from these studies is that the more we seek external validation, the less satisfied we are.

An ACL injury is a traumatic event. I will never claim anything but this truth. This truth does make it pertinent to note that in times of trauma, especially due to the potential loss of roles/self, we find ourselves operating almost entirely under the pretense of our conceptualized self. This is harmful because it detaches us from our reality. For example, our transcendent self could cling to the fact that we are solely an athlete, and that is all we will ever be. Our true self understands that we will not always be an athlete, and it helps us prepare for our life after sports. If everything that makes us who we are is taken from us, humans tend to engage in self-harming behavior, like abusing drugs, neglecting our other obligations, etc.

The self-pivot is important, similar to the other five. Like completing a perfectly executed play or strategy, all components must be aligned to function to the fullest. To take the first step down this path, you need to mindfully put all your efforts into finding external acceptance and use it appropriately to reconnect with your transcendent self in the present. In living where your knees are, you can be present in each moment, allowing yourself to connect meaningfully to yourself and others.

The importance of self-pivoting, identifying, and staying true to our transcendent selves cannot be overstated. In returning to one's transcendent self, we are returning home. In returning to the true self, we find purpose and meaning in living where our knees are. If we cannot even identify our true selves, attempting to compete and function the way we used to, before surgery or injury, will be much more difficult.

Much like any important set of skills, the skills listed above build on each other, like algebra or legos (I will let you pick the metaphor you prefer). To begin down the road of perspective-taking, you must first utilize defusion to notice and distance yourself from your "conceptualized self" stories. Being present and taking note of your perspective will ensure that you understand that you are separate from your thoughts. Various perspective-taking exercises can shift your ability to relate to the time, place, and people around you.

Like the defusion techniques, you can learn various techniques to incorporate into your daily routine to practice the self-pivot. Personally, I have utilized these techniques to pass the time while icing, during film sessions, and (again) commercial breaks. Although some writing and conversation activities may be pertinent, it is still notable that no one would even know you are working on these skills (unless, of course, you wish to reveal your transcendent self to a trusted confidant).

The development of your transcendent self, like the other pivots, is a life-long journey. I fall off the path daily, but I can brush myself off and refocus on the path of acceptance.

Chapter 9: Acceptance

"The first step toward change is awareness. The second step is acceptance."

–Nathaniel Branden

They say the first step in any recovery journey is admitting there is a problem. In my opinion (while that statement does compute), the first real mark of emotional healing and making a lasting change is adding and continually working on sharpening acceptance skills. In the previous chapters, we discussed the idea of defusing our thoughts and our "true" self. This foundation will continue to be built upon as we discuss acceptance in greater detail.

Many miraculous seasons have numerous ups and downs associated with them. A season in sports is comparable, on many levels, to life. A team experiences moments of joy, victory, and celebration. The comradery, communication, and goal-oriented work, which is imperative to any successful team, are similar to our personal lives.

We have moments when we all do things well, and the reason we achieved whatever we sought after is due to our inherent skills, principles, and work ethic. Similarly, if the team has competing interests, a lack of cohesion, and a poor work ethic, it is likely that the season will not go as planned. Not practicing acceptance skills personally is like a coach following an unsuccessful strategy to win games and continuing to do so due to their inability to accept that it was a poor idea in the first place. If we cannot accept that what we are doing is not taking us where we want to go, it is paramount that we take a step back and acknowledge it. This acknowledgment leads to accepting our misbehavior, shortcomings, and difficulties. This helps ensure we move along a different, more appropriate path in the future.

One thing I have always been good at is hiding my feelings. I function at a reasonably high level for someone with severe anxiety, and I have always taken pride in that. For the longest time, I thought that to function properly, I had to suppress my feelings. I had to "be normal" and pursue perpetual numbness.

One particular moment in which I majorly failed in this endeavor occurred when I arrived home from the orthopedic surgeon, who confirmed my deepest fears. This was the moment when I had to admit to myself that I could no longer pursue my dream of playing professionally in either the Canadian Football League (CFL) or the National Football League (NFL). This dream had been the outgrowth of what that little boy had wanted as he watched his father passionately play basketball during his childhood. Football was to me as basketball was to my father. It was an effortless game built on grit, instincts, and physical attributes that I was luckily blessed with. As I said before, I loved football. It transported me across the country, helped me get an education, gave me everlasting friendships, and taught me countless life lessons.

After returning home from the orthopedic surgeon after my second ACL injury, I remember feeling the leather couch beneath me. I remember the hole in my chest growing until it consumed me. I felt all the pain I had suppressed and the hope I had accumulated over the past weeks dissipate. I had, all at once, lost the ability to continue to push toward my athletic goals. That pain poured from my eyes in front of my family. They had watched me train incessantly for two years following my previous injury. Now, this part of my life was over. Although I was far from achieving psychological flexibility at that point in my life, that moment was an important one that led me to the schooling and training necessary to achieve my newfound purpose, all thanks to acceptance.

One of the most impactful lessons I learned from Dr. Hayes's book, *A Liberated Mind*, is discussed in great detail on the acceptance pivot. It was not only on acceptance, which is decently straightforward, but also on humans' inherent need to feel. Emotional avoidance denies us the yearning to feel, and Dr. Hayes points out that feeling is "the key to our survival—not only in helping us learn about dangers but in guiding us to the sources of joy and fulfillment."[75] We spend much of our waking time searching for literature, art, music, or any form of entertainment that makes us feel.

A point that is especially applicable for athletes who undergo ACL surgery is that while athletes yearn to feel, all humans have a threshold in which they are uncomfortable passing. Many times, the sport that we are willing to put our body through can cause more psychological pain when it is threatened or taken from us permanently. Acceptance allows us to feel and learn from both the negative and positive emotions that exist outside of our comfort zone. This may seem difficult, and truthfully, it is. This pivot took me the longest to understand, hone, and master.

To this day, I continue to work on accepting various parts of my life that are both negative and positive, and I consider the benefits both sides have presented to me. For instance, my previous ACL surgeries, countless hours searching for resources online, and training consistently in different ways to determine what works best for my condition have made me somewhat obsessed with those who have undergone ACL surgery, similar to me. It has ignited a passion in me that I do not hold for anything else on this earth.

I have a mission to help provide therapy, coaching, and any assistance I can (emotionally or physically) to those who have had this injury. Whether I have met them or not, I instantly feel connected with someone who has had an ACL injury. I know what they have felt, endured, and likely continue to feel. I needed to accept the ending of one phase of my life and my inner yearning to feel in order to connect with all of you. Knowing what I know now, I feel I can assist many of you in overcoming the hurdles necessary for your recovery—and hopefully save your career or lead you in a direction that will provide just as much meaning.

If you can't accept the gifts of the past, you cannot prepare for the ills of the future. Life is messy, and unfortunately, it will always be so. Not learning from the past will only ensure additional, similar pain will be had in the future. For example, even though you followed everything the athletic trainer or physical therapist instructed, you still got hurt again. In the next situation (knock on wood), would you only do what they said, or would you seek additional help in conjunction with theirs?

"Insanity is doing the same thing over and over and expecting different results."

–Unknown

Acceptance is a crucial skill on the path to recovery from an ACL injury, and it helps in everyday life. Being psychologically inflexible hinders positive change and can lead to poor decisions that result in negative consequences. Pragmatically speaking, acceptance is key to allowing oneself to achieve what one needs and wants. Therefore, the purpose of acceptance goes far beyond the scope of just ACL injuries.

While this notion is paramount on your route to psychological flexibility, it is important to get a reasonable handle on your "defusion" and "self" skills prior. This is because they all build upward like a tower, leading you to your ideal self. If you do not have the appropriate foundation, it can be difficult to climb anywhere.

Acceptance is a fundamental skill for anyone struggling with the physical and emotional difficulties an

ACL injury presents. If this skill can ensure you're on the path to psychological flexibility, just like stopping in the middle of a play in football and goal kick in soccer, it is important to be mindful and finish your perspective task in athletics. The same is true for pivoting toward a healthier you.

Chapter 10: Mindfulness

"Worrying about the past or the future isn't productive. When you start chastising yourself for past mistakes, or seeing disaster around every corner, stop and take a breath and ask yourself what you can do right now to succeed."

–Harvey Mackay

Recently, I came across an article written by Mitchell Newberry, a Professor of Complex Systems at the University of Michigan. His article conveniently discussed chaos. When we, as humans, think of chaos, I believe we tend to think of novels or movies we have read or watched.

We think of war, psychological thrillers, or components of magic. Newberry notes, "In a chaotic world, you never know what to expect. Stuff is happening all the time, driven by any kind of random impulse."[76] Does that situation sound familiar? It sounds very much like the current environment we all find ourselves in. The article also notes that the scientific definition of chaos can be described as "the amplified effects of tiny changes in the present moment that lead to long-term unpredictability." Consider any time-traveling scenario you have read in a book or watched in a movie or TV series. Even the most minute divergence from the previous "reality" can create an entirely new one.

Many think that the small details don't matter, but as Newberry notes, "Sometimes tiny differences have consequences that keep compounding. And that compounding is what leads to chaos." [77]

You may feel as though your world is currently in chaos. Rightly so, I'd say. We live in a time where the world and country are highly politicized, making any interaction highly volatile. We also live in a time where we have countless distractions.

Another article that piqued my interest was by Charlie Ohlen regarding technology and its numerous impacts on various generations. The invention of smartphones has led us to become used to constant entertainment, connection, and distraction. Obviously, there are positive aspects to these devices, but the advances that have led to their creation come with consequences. Ohlen stated in his article, "Outside of—internet trolls, bullying, and mental health issues spawning from social media's exclusive metrics and design—we've seen the attention span of grade-schoolers and teens drop drastically."[78] While the COVID-19 pandemic raged out of control across the globe, did we let another digital pandemic flourish for roughly a decade? This chaos can lead even those who are not experiencing trying times to struggle emotionally, let alone someone who has undergone an ACL injury.

"Be where your feet are."

–Tom Coughlin (to the Giants)

While that quote from Tom Coughlin is short, it provides the overall thought process for this entire pivot. This chapter discusses mindfulness and living, literally, where our feet (and knees) are.

Sweating and sore, I settled into what had become a popular position for myself. My leg was elevated, compressed, and being iced. I had just gone through a particularly difficult rehabilitation session with the athletic trainer. Once again, I did not achieve the physical goal necessary to move to the next rehabilitation stage. I remember looking at my phone, trying to distract myself from the barrage of my teammates around the training room getting taped for the upcoming practice.

The laughter, jokes, and excitement that filled the room were always palpable before practice. Acting as though everything was okay, and that I wasn't deeply hurt, was always a momentous chore. Sometimes, I felt as though that took just as much out of me as my physical rehabilitation. As my teammates left, I couldn't help but feel a pit in my stomach and a hole in my chest. I was missing another day of doing what I love due to my inability to stay healthy.

I daydreamed almost constantly about simply returning to practice. Feeling the thrill of competing in my sport with my teammates. While these thoughts always began with a positive connotation, they never ended positively. In these daydreams, I would be running just as I used to, smiling and enjoying what I was meant to do. The daydream would then cut to a loop of me tearing my ACL again. No matter what I pictured myself doing, I would end up feeling that audible pop and collapse, to my dismay. Have you ever seen the famous workout montages of the "Rocky" movies? Picture a similar montage, but instead of someone triumphantly breaking down physical barriers, imagine the opposite. A loop of the worst thing that has happened to you physically, occurring over and over. A future in which I could compete was all I wanted, but it was also everything I feared. I had numerous negative thoughts that many of you can likely relate to:

"If I can't even do this, how can I ever run or compete again?"

"What if I never get better?"

"Will this pain ever go away?"

"How pathetic I have become; I can't even straighten or bend my leg the way I used to."

While the thought of the future gave me anxiety and continued to make my physical therapy and training stressful, thoughts of the past did little more to comfort me.

Other times, when I would daydream or get caught in my thoughts, I would drift backward in time. I would think about how well I played a certain game or practice and relive those "glorious moments" we all have as athletes. They used to provide comfort and excitement for the future. Surely, if I did it once, I could replicate that perfect play, game, or season. Right? The more I thought about this, the more I was bombarded with deep depressive thoughts and the reminder that, actually, I might never be able to do it again.

The question then becomes: if I cannot look ahead and I cannot look back to gain contentment, focus, and psychological flexibility, where CAN I look? The answer is to focus solely, to the best of your ability, on where you are now. As Tom Coughlin said, "Live where your feet are." For us specifically, I think it is more fitting for it to read: "Live where your knees are." The most effective way to do this is to start practicing mindfulness.

Mindfulness is the basic ability to be fully present, aware of what we're doing and where we are, and not overly reactive or overwhelmed by what's happening around us.[79]

That may seem like a simple task. As I mentioned, though, the world is chaotic. Not only is the overarching world chaotic, but you are likely at a chaotic point in your life, making it doubly hard to live and operate fully at the moment. As humans, we tend to lose touch with our bodies, thoughts, emotions, and feelings and perseverate on the past or anxieties about the future. Mindfulness can be used as a tether to the present, to how we are currently doing physically or feeling emotionally. As you might have guessed, this is an innate capability that humans possess, but it can only be properly utilized with the appropriate practice so you can readily access it.[80]

Even though out of necessity, Google Trends for "mindfulness" has been steadily increasing recently, the skill was invented a very long time ago.[81] Literature has stated that the history and evolution of mindfulness can be traced back 2,500 years. Many people commonly think that mindfulness originated in Buddhism, but it actually extends much further back in history, dating back to the practices of the Hindu people.

Researchers believe that the Hindu religion began between 2300 BC and 1500 BC in the Indus Valley, near modern Pakistan; therefore, pre-Buddhism by a substantial margin. Mindfulness migrated from Eastern religion to the modern West, largely due to Jon Kabat-Zinn. Zinn was first introduced to the practice while in graduate school to obtain his Ph.D. in molecular biology at the Massachusetts Institute of Technology (MIT). In 1979, he founded the Mindfulness-Based Stress Reduction (MBSR) Clinic at the University of Massachusetts Medical Center. Zinn, who would produce multiple literary works on mindfulness, used his scientific research to depict the benefits of mindfulness, bringing global attention to his work.[82]

Mindfulness has been around for a long time, but why is it important to you? If we followed other practices or skills founded thousands of years ago, it is unlikely many would warrant your attention. I feel mindfulness is different and has been imperative to my psychological flexibility journey. This pivot has allowed me to function more optimally despite my personal trauma and ACL injuries. The question is: how can mindfulness help me in my current situation?

Mindfulness has been found to have numerous positive effects on those who practice it. I have found through my current practice that the efficacy of the skill grows over time. Much like anything else, the better you are at a skill, the more effective it is in practice.

A recent meta-analysis evaluated 136 trials, including 11,605 participants across 29 countries. This particular study analyzed the effect of mindfulness-based programs on their ability to reduce stress in a non-clinical setting. Compared to passive control groups, mindfulness-based programs improved anxiety, depression, psychological distress, and mental well-being. The most substantial results were decreased anxiety, depression, and psychological distress. The improvement in mental well-being wasn't as strongly correlated.[83]

Another study found that mindfulness-based stress reduction was an effective intervention that can improve the psychological functioning of another high-stress population.[84]

Evidence suggests that mindfulness can be useful not only for emotional health, but also for cognitive function. A recent meta-analysis suggests that there is primary evidence that mindfulness can improve executive functioning.[85] Executive functioning is a collection of mental skills that include self-control, flexible thinking, and working memory. These skills are necessary to learn, work, and complete daily activities; trouble with any of these skills could make it difficult to handle emotions, focus, and follow directions.

Mindfulness has also been linked to a number of physiological benefits that would be advantageous for athletes who are overcoming an injury or returning to play. A recent randomized control trial demonstrated that the intervention group, who practiced mindfulness consistently over an eight-week period, produced lower ambulatory blood pressure than the control group, as well as lower systolic blood pressure. In addition to the physiological changes in this study, the intervention group also noticed improvements, including being less judgmental, more accepting, and less depressed.[86]

Another study found that mindfulness-based interventions can reliably enhance attention, as well as executive control, to some extent.[87]

While the emotional, cognitive, and physiological benefits of mindfulness are important, many athletes, including myself, are interested in the effect it could have on athletic performance. Athletes tend to analyze the things that take up a significant amount of time daily to determine if they benefit what is important to them. For example, as athletes, we prioritize healthy food and hydrate routinely to ensure that we are primed for competition at any time.

Likewise, we prioritize relationships that we perceive benefit us; otherwise, we likely would not put the effort in due to lack of time. The same will be asked of these pivots, including mindfulness. If we put a constant amount of time and energy into this skill, how will it benefit us in the future? Humans, and obviously athletes, are inherently strategic in how they spend their time. We tend to spend time doing what is important to us, so if mindfulness displays that capability, it is likely to be widely accepted. Something that would strengthen the likelihood that it would be widely adopted is the effect these skills would have on athletic performance.

Multiple recent studies have shown a relationship between successful athletes and mindfulness. One such study analyzed 2,013 athletes competing at the national and international levels in track and field. The findings of this study determined that the athletes with high performance had higher mindfulness levels compared to the athletes with low performance levels.[88] These findings are consistent with another study by Hill et al., where they found runners who performed mindfulness exercises had higher athletic performance development rates than those who did not.[89] Similar results were garnered from both the Birrer et al. and Dehghani et al. studies, continuing to display the effectiveness of these skills on athletes' athletic performance.[90,91]

Mindfulness, in my opinion, has the potential to change the course of your rehabilitation drastically. Maybe it will not affect all ACL survivors, but I can speak for myself and attest that it has really redirected my mental and psychological health. If you are following this series on ACL rehabilitation, then you know that your personal narrative plays a significant role in how you adapt to the challenges of knee injury and ACL reconstruction. The Mindfulness pivot is imperative to establishing a healthy narrative, allowing us to achieve the highest level of personal growth. The goal is not to become a robot or mindless being, but rather to reduce resistance to change and enhance our experiences positively.

The question now becomes: have ACT-focused mindfulness-based programs been developed specifically for us, as ACL survivors?

Unfortunately, no.

While that is frustrating, I can say that is only the case presently. I will be developing and providing specific mindfulness programs tailored to ACL survivors and the struggles they encounter throughout their journey in the not-so-distant future.

Like the other pivots, I plan to have all components condensed into avenues that can be easily utilized by athletes on the go, whether that is between classes, in the training room, or on the bus. It is important to remember that anything worth doing is worth doing poorly initially. At the beginning of my journey, I daresay I was as bad as you can possibly be at mindfulness. However, I have drastically improved my skills and use them regularly to provide the assistance I need to function and complete everything I want to do on a typical day. This is what I want for you and what you will get to should you continue to buy into the process and these pivots.

The most important thing to note about mindfulness is that it can be altered and digested in a way that is most conducive to your preference. Tailoring how you incorporate all the pivots described in this book is crucial to the efficacy of this therapeutic technique. This cannot be done without taking a deeper look at your own personal values.

Chapter 11: Personal Values

"Values are like fingerprints. Nobody's are the same, but you leave 'em all over everything you do."

–Elvis Presley

If you are like me, you have lived your entire life being force-fed the idea that, in order to be successful, you have to set goals and work toward achieving them. While this is partly true, it is also inherently partly false. Setting goals is important to achieving what you want in this life. Goal-setting is a widely discussed topic, but I feel the current conversation is insufficient.

I have spent the better part of my adulthood chasing goals in all facets of my life (relationships, academics, athletics, spirituality, etc.). After finding both success and failure in the pursuit of these goals, I have learned one fundamental thing that contradicted everything I thought I knew about goal-setting. I used to believe goals were the stepping stones to the outcomes I desired, but now I know that goals are the milestones on the trail of our values. A value is a life direction, an internal compass that guides us throughout life. Values are different from goals that have an endpoint. Values are often life-long and give life meaning and purpose. Some might think that the best way to describe someone's values is by looking at what they want to be remembered for.

To discover your core beliefs, consider what is most essential in your life and what gives it meaning and purpose.

A fault of mine that I have become quite acquainted with throughout my psychological journey is the feeling of emptiness. I have had the opportunity to pursue and sometimes achieve my goals. One thing that remained consistent is that I often felt empty or completely apathetic when I "achieved" a goal I set out for.

I couldn't figure out why that was and mainly attributed it to my struggles with mental illness. Through my journey with ACT and psychological flexibility, I discovered that this could be one of two reasons:

1. I was not pursuing goals that were congruent with my values; or,

2. My outlook was incorrect regarding the goals themselves.

I, as well as many others, tend to think of goals as a destination or a point at which I will finally feel "fulfilled." This could not be farther from the truth. For example, after graduating with my doctoral degree, it was a monumental goal of mine to pay off all of my debt associated with that degree. The total amount of this debt was nearly $100,000. Like many throughout the United States, I knew that this debt could negatively impact my future family.

After clawing and scraping, I was able to pay this amount off in a reasonable amount of time. I was able to remove this anchor from my financial life. When I paid the final balance of my debt, I remember feeling strangely unaccomplished. It was a peculiar feeling, as I had achieved what many wish to do, but I still didn't feel as accomplished as I thought I would.

I had similar feelings when I got signed to an arena football team and when I received word that I had passed my licensure exam, making me a licensed occupational therapist. If I had attained these goals, why wasn't I feeling the accomplishment or contentment I thought would come with it?

This is something I pondered for a long time. I went to therapy, worked on self-care, stuck to a regular workout regimen, and prioritized my nutrition. None of these things seemed to alleviate the emptiness I felt through completing these goals. The realization came after stumbling upon ACT.

Acceptance and Commitment Therapy (ACT) led me to heal from past trauma and understand why I had these feelings of emptiness. Through ACT, I learned that I had adopted the values of those around me—such as society at large, my religion, and my family. In many cases, this is beneficial, but it is important to note that even those you are close with may have slightly or drastically different values than you. They are unique to each of us.

Nowadays, with our fast-paced and, at times, chaotic lives, it is natural to run on autopilot and neglect to truly assess whether we are living the values-based life tailored toward ourselves. It is only when we live our lives according to our values that we can be at peace. For me, this wasn't the knowledge that alleviated the emptiness that persisted through my late teens and twenties, but also the knowledge that goals are not destinations. As I stated before, goals are the milestones on the trail of our values. We never truly "arrive" at our destinations. However, learning that goals are milestones on the path of *our* choosing in our lives can drastically increase the satisfaction felt by accomplishing various goals in life.

For myself, when I paid off my previous debt, I learned how to look at it through the lens of my values. Instead of feeling empty at accomplishing my goal, I was able to take the next step in my financial journey: saving for an emergency fund. Life happens, and emergencies come up, and I did not want that to be devastating to my current situation. I felt comfort in knowing that these goals would prevent my future family from feeling the financial stress that permeated my childhood and adolescent years. I want to provide a life for my future family that is void of any financial stress and have the opportunity to grow our family legacy in an uncertain world.

Dr. Moran, an ACT researcher, describes the necessity for values to be utilized for optimal psychological flexibility by relating life to a journey. "Every journey requires that you move forward step by step, moment by moment."[92] The cool thing is you get to choose a direction for each step: north, south, east, west. There isn't a right step to take, just a chosen step, which is entirely up to you. Now, if we were in a session and discussed all the ways to direct your behavior, and you decided that you'd prefer to go east, I'd first congratulate you on the decision. The next step would be formulating goals that lead you along the path you'd like to follow. There are plenty of resources for goal-setting, such as SMART goals, that would be helpful here.

While this topic might seem straightforward, it is quite effective in use. The book *Mindfulness and Acceptance: Expanding the Cognitive-Behavioral Tradition* states values interventions direct therapy or coaching by targeting exposure and defusion events that function as barriers to valued living. Hayes and his colleagues further note, "When obstacles prevent movement in the valued domain, targeting those obstacles with exposure and defusion strategies aimed at building a broad and flexible skillset provide positive outcomes."[93] Another study further confirmed the efficacy of values-based therapy in chronic pain. The study produced significant improvements in emotional and physical functioning relative to baseline, as well as good maintenance of treatment gains relative to earlier follow-up assessment. At the three-year follow-up, 64.8 percent of patients had reliably improved in at least one key domain.[94]

Many of us make goals, but few follow through with those goals. Think of the infamous "New Year's Resolutioners" who make it a grand total of three weeks into January before relinquishing all hope of achieving their goal. Why do you think that is? I believe it is due to their inability to attach goals to their values and WHY they are looking to achieve the specific goal.

I believe making the pivot into this thought process and determining what your unique values are can ignite your ability to fast-track your recovery from various ailments, including ACL tears. The entire rehabilitation process is overwhelming, but it can be less so if you incorporate this pivot. Although I am no longer in rehabilitation for my knee, I still use these concepts in my particular values to direct my steps in personal therapy and daily living. It is more than a resolution. Rather, it is an entire commitment to the process of healing and recovery for your future self, values, and relationships.

While this takes mindful concentration, through the correct coaching or therapy, it is quite possible. Certain activities can help hone your knowledge and understanding of your unique values. Further understanding our values, how they shape us, how they were formed, and why we have each specific value only increases our ability to act in accordance with these values. This way of acting helps us embody the mission we are on as individuals.

Chapter 12: Action

"Peace of mind produces right values; right values produce right thoughts. Right thoughts produce right actions."

–Mark Richardson

"If admitting you have a problem is the first step to recovery, then action is the marathon that ensues."

–Keagen Hadley (The Author)

The carpet felt particularly coarse against my cheek as I opened my eyes to the world. I had no idea how long I had been passed out. Judging from the past, it could have been twenty minutes or four hours, but it was impossible to tell at the moment. I peeled myself off of the carpet of my closet and looked around, trying to determine what had happened. As per usual, the adjoined master bathroom/closet was strewn with clothes on the floor, various garbage, and the ever-present empty alcohol bottles. I didn't have to look long before seeing the empty liter next to me, answering what had happened. Between the bottle and the spinning room, anyone could have solved that mystery.

I proceeded to get dressed, trying to ignore the mirror and the reflection of the malnourished individual who routinely returned my gaze. I can still remember the hunger and unwillingness to eat. I would spend days hoping that maybe this time, I'd be able to last long enough to stop the pain. I did have the intuition to minimize the hunger before grad school exams, not because I feared for my performance, but because I had long given up any hope of being a therapist. I just had anxiety that my classmates would hear my stomach during the quietness that came in tandem with exams. At this point, I had lost 40 pounds over the last year while ignoring the worry of my family and friends.

I would regularly drive, take tests, and generally perform any other daily activities drunk. Not out of choice or addiction, but out of what I thought was my way of saving my girlfriend at the time (more so, her son). As I alluded to earlier, she was an alcoholic and, unfortunately for me, quite manipulative. Looking back, it is quite a unique experience to see where my life truly was at this time. Unless one has been in an emotionally abusive situation, they wouldn't understand how someone eventually gets to be where I was.

Most individuals (understandably) would think I still had a choice and won't understand. I was still under the presumption she would return to the person I knew her to be before the alcohol took over her life. My positivity turned into a negative personality trait during this time and prolonged my pain since it continued to foster this false hope. My hope, while shrinking daily, is what kept me around as long as I was, and I couldn't face the reality that I didn't know how to help her.

The copious amounts of alcohol and temptation for her were always seemingly present in our apartment.

This situation always ended up being a threat: "Either you drink this, or I'll kill myself." As things escalated, so would her actions, depending on whether or not she had indulged her addiction. To this day, I still worry about drinking alcohol for fear of becoming addicted. I am not sure how I escaped that, but it still is an adamant fear I am working through with my therapist. In this period of my life, I felt stuck, worthless, and hopeless. I blamed this situation on others. Although I was not fully to blame, it was my life. Getting out of any situation is ultimately up to you—and the actions you take.

Much like with any ailment or injury, I had to seek help. I got to the point where I had finally had enough and separated from that highly toxic relationship. I soon found out that, although I had removed the rot of that relationship from my life, I would carry a part of it with me forever. To continue to move down the path I chose and continue to choose daily will take routine, mindfulness, and action. I accepted I could no longer go through all of those emotions alone, and I sought help from a therapist for myself and this situation. This therapist was my guide to betterment and happiness, and it occurred due to purposeful action.

Action is helpful and paramount to psychological flexibility, regardless of the type of trauma (loss of a loved one, addiction, tearing your ACL, or other injuries, etc.). Numerous scholarly articles display the efficacy of such purposeful action. Peterson et al. demonstrated that those who followed purposeful, problem-solving actions had a strong negative correlation with depression levels.[95] This finding was not found in those who used avoidance or other coping mechanisms. The purposeful action pathway is the ideal path to follow, as it has positive mental health outcomes. However, it is not easy.

This knowledge has been widely available for decades. More research, provided by Susan Nolen-Hoeksema, found that depressive episodes were drastically abbreviated if patients avoided rumination, focusing on causes and their symptoms, but rather took purposeful action to ensure their mind was occupied by other means.[96] This may come from exercise, work, or anything else you enjoy. If you are having a particularly hard time locating something you enjoy, think about what you would want to do if money were no object. This is a bit of an extreme, but it helps me to place my mind back in the present and focus on something I want to do, not what I should be doing.

For additional ideas on finding areas in your life in which you are truly interested (e.g., a hobby or constructive outlet to place your attention or energy), please visit my blog at keagenhadley.com.

Purposeful action is a proactive response to any psychologically challenging scenario. When faced with challenging events, those who take positive, active approaches have been shown to suffer from less psychological distress than those who do not use such coping mechanisms. I believe that if you are struggling with any sort of mental health difficulties, it is important to be mindful of your thought patterns and actions. Using purposeful action can help you achieve happiness if practiced regularly. This is not because purposeful action is a magical pill that alleviates all problems, but rather because anyone moving toward what is meaningful to them is inherently more content than those who are stagnant or moving in the wrong direction.

It is imperative to take action to get through any challenge—not just emotional or psychological issues, but also physical problems like ACL tears. Like ACL tears, psychological distress is not something you can simply get over. It requires daily effort to maintain your well-being. Taking purposeful action is an important step that every ACL tear survivor should take into consideration when attempting to achieve happiness or move toward their goals.[97,98]

Not only can purposeful action assist in athletes' mental or emotional injuries, but it has also been found to have a significant effect on the physical rehabilitation of its users. A study by Kim found that stroke patients who performed or observed purposeful actions had significantly improved upper extremity function compared to the placebo group.[99]

Action directed toward valued goals gives life purpose, implying that people's self-esteem is linked to their sense of purpose. To attain our goals, we must identify what we want to accomplish and how best to pursue it, and then follow through and intentionally act according to our goals.[100]

What is the role of purpose in achieving one's objectives? Is it to help us get closer to our aspirations, or are there other factors at play? Does meaning come from striving toward positive outcomes or both? Could the concept of purpose be a mechanism for linking individuals' behavior to their subjective happiness? Three studies showed that purpose was positively predicted by action but negatively by individual planning (i.e., paralysis analysis).[101] Paralysis analysis is a situation in which one "plans" to do something, and because they continue to plan or "analyze," they continue to be inactive, never actually acting on the analyses or plans. The research by Vazeou-Nieuwenhuis demonstrates that purpose is derived from *action*, and action has significance.[102]

ACT encourages the development of more and larger patterns of successful activities that are linked to valued principles. ACT, in this regard, resembles traditional behavioral therapy. Almost any behaviorally coherent behavior change technique can be included in an ACT plan, including exposure, skill acquisition, shaping methods, goal-setting, etc. Values are constantly instantiated but never achieved as an object. Goals that are consistent with values can be more easily attainable. ACT therapy usually involves homework linked to short-, medium-, and long-term behavior change goals for therapy. Behavior changes lead to contact with psychological barriers that can be addressed by other ACT processes, creating a circle or dance in which one pivot may lead to another, allowing you to move through your day and life fluently.

Implementing the action pivot will be slightly different than the other pivots. It will be a full-time job. A commitment is an action, and the word "commitment" is a noun, but it's the kind of noun that requires action. As ACL tear survivors, we want to ensure our behavior does not delay our rehabilitation and return to the activities we love. When you're committed to this kind of task, process, or direction, you can keep moving in that direction with your actions. You just keep moving with your actions, over the problem, around it, or beneath it. Action is required to demonstrate your resolve. This may seem like a monumental task. Frankly, it is. However, it can be broken down into digestible bite-sized pieces. Future courses, along with my upcoming private practice, will delve into those issues and make them easy for you to utilize and continually practice.

An ACL tear requires a lengthy recovery protocol to return to previous activity levels, competition, and function. Emotional and psychological healing will also be a difficult endeavor. ACL injuries are not simple, but the healing process with ACT is. With purposeful action steps, you can be efficient with your time and efforts.[103,104]

Chapter 13: Part 2 Overview

"To finish first, you must first finish."

–Rick Mears

My intention for the second part of this book is for you, the reader, to be able to dig deeper into the specific issues that you face at particular points in your journey.

In each chapter, we will go over what could be bothering you and how using ACT will decrease the overall effect of your symptoms. Whether you are aware or not, these symptoms affect your ability to regain previous function and truly excel in your rehabilitation.

Throughout my four surgeries involving both knees (and ACLs), I have encountered some variation of all the issues I will discuss in the following chapters. The good news is that I was able to get past all of them through ACT. While I am far from perfect, the skills I learned from ACT allow me to live as full of a life as possible following the trauma of an ACL injury.

The core values of ACT are observing your thoughts, acknowledging your "true" self, acceptance, mindfulness, aligning with your values, and purposeful action. These pillars will provide the structure needed to address the pain, hurt, and discomfort regarding your current psychological situation associated with your knee injury.

One of my personal goals with the second part of this book is for your self-awareness to grow. This way, you can begin applying the concepts I have outlined to minimize the negative psychological impacts on your ACL recovery. It is important that we acknowledge our reality and accept where we are personally on the psychological flexibility continuum. Depending on how foreign each of the previous ACT components has felt to you, you may want to continue to hone your ideology of the pivots of ACT. If necessary, reach out for guidance or further training in these methods.

Without further ado, let's dive into what could be delaying your rehabilitation.

Chapter 14: Depression, Poor Coping, and Lack of Motivation

"Pain moves us forward, changing us into something else, something we need to be."

–Michelle Moran

Depression is an interesting, complex, and misunderstood condition. People tend to assume the most detrimental symptom is decreased mood or helplessness. While this is a substantial hurdle for individuals and athletes to overcome, there is another aspect that is supremely challenging to athletes' overall well-being.

Avolition, or lack/loss of motivation, can negatively impact individuals with ACL injuries due to the quick change in daily activities associated with the injury. As an athlete, you go from competing at a high level, being fully self-sufficient, and being driven to compete against your peers or adversaries to potentially having difficulty simply getting up in the morning.

This lack of motivation, coupled with poor coping skills, can lead to vastly delayed rehabilitation time, not meeting personal or therapists' goals, and potentially lifelong negative habits that could impact all other facets of affected individuals' lives.

If you ever saw me and watched how I act on a normal basis, you would never think I've had any struggles with depression. I joke, laugh, and smile my way through the majority of my days. As I alluded to earlier, that is my normal. While that may be true, I have had a dramatic shift in how I feel and relate to others. Over the last number of years, I have been overwhelmed with grief, pain, and sadness that manifested into a numbness that seemed to persist no matter the situation.

Prior to ACT, I would test the bounds of what I could do to myself, or to others, and still be void of any feeling. I would drink, smoke, and do almost anything to feel. I just wanted to become myself again after a part of me was taken away. I, like many others, put up a front that I wasn't struggling or wasn't bothered by my situation. I was doing precisely the opposite of what would help me out of my situation during this portion of my life. Unfortunately, these poor coping mechanisms and the avolition I endured are common among ACL survivors.

I spent most of my childhood, adolescence, and young adulthood hyper-focusing on physical skills and attributes. These physical challenges provided a necessary outlet for me to maintain adequate mental health. When I lost those outlets, I quickly learned that I had not developed any mental skills or tools to deal with the pain, grief, and anger I had grown accustomed to. This led to the behaviors mentioned above. Fortunately, I pivoted to utilize other coping methods before forming an addiction or causing any permanent damage to myself. What I regret most is how I treated those close to me due to my inability to cope, depression, and anger.

I remember a specific situation that perfectly demonstrates the new lows I found while in this stage of my ACL recovery.

It was the Friday before the last game of the season my senior year. I, of course, was found to be ineligible (due to the aforementioned transfer credit issue) after working tirelessly to recover after my first ACL tear. This particular day, I was supposed to be starting my training for my first arena football league combine. Although I had many months, I knew that I should be prioritizing this training for not only my physical health, but also my mental health. I had rapidly gone from training incessantly to having difficulty gathering the motivation to train. While I had made sizeable improvements in my strength and movement that had been taken from me due to the injury, I still had a lot of work to do to regain my full athletic ability.

Removing the chance to compete with my teammates destroyed me. I became something that I never thought I would. I became completely and utterly unmotivated due to depression and a lack of hope. I spent most of that day drinking, smoking, and chasing emotions I could never find. This search lasted long into the night and as night faded to morning. In the process, I tore my pants, lost my key card, and lost a friend. The tile felt nearly as cold as the air outside when I woke up. The kitchen dormitory is definitely not a spot I highly recommend. The buzzing and newly cracked phone signaled that I was late to the game I never wanted to see. That morning, I realized I had an issue coping with my pain and depression. I knew that, until I dealt with those feelings, I would continue to be unmotivated, unhappy, and have no purpose.

As I watched the game, I became acutely aware that this was a rock bottom point in my life. Although the pain continued throughout the game, including the announcement of myself and the other seniors, I accepted where I was. To this day, it is one of the hardest things I have ever done. Up until that point, I had blamed everyone else in my life for the position I was in. I blamed my academic advisor for not following my credits more closely. I blamed my coach for not following up on my transfer credits and also for the ridiculous amount of conditioning from fall camp that (in my mind) led to my ACL tear. Although these people hadn't helped me, I knew that they had not put me in the current emotional situation I was in. It is fair to note that, no matter your situation, the person in the mirror is likely to blame. This was my case, and it might also be yours.

Depression, as we know, is very serious, regardless of the situation that coerced it to present. Not only is it serious, but it is, unfortunately, very prevalent in Western cultures. Depression among adults in the United States tripled in the early months of the 2020 global coronavirus pandemic—jumping from 8.5 percent before the pandemic to a staggering 27.8 percent. New research from the Boston University School of Public Health reveals that the elevated rate of depression has persisted into 2021 and even worsened, climbing to 32.8 percent and affecting one in every three American adults.[105] Depression is so common that it is difficult to turn on the TV or browse the internet without seeing an advertisement for pharmaceuticals, over-the-counter medications, or various other treatments for depression.[106]

Additionally, the media tends to sensationalize depression. For example, instances of suicide tend to describe victims' unsuccessful battle against depression. Not only are the fatalities associated with depression sensationalized, but also the effects of the aforementioned treatments. It is common for people who have "recovered" from depression to be depicted as having blissful lives presenting no residual difficulties associated with depression. Not only are these depictions misleading, but they also cause additional depression associated with seeking treatment. The message is always the same: "Get your life back," "…so you can start living again," etc. This signals to individuals struggling with depression that, in order to live a productive life, they have to control their depression.[107] This is simply not the case. Depression is a complex psychological issue, and no two people present or experience it precisely the same way. Therefore, there is no "cure" or quick fix, but rather a change of mind that allows you to take control of your decisions and your life.[108]

A recent study found that there is a substantial correlation between ACL injury and post-traumatic stress disorder (PTSD) symptomology. The study found that more than 87.5 percent of patients experienced avoidance symptoms, 83.3 percent acknowledged symptoms of intrusion, and 75 percent had symptoms of hyperarousal.[109] This statistic should not come as much of a surprise to anyone who has sustained an ACL injury, as it is a very traumatic experience.

Trauma and depression may seem like opposites, but they actually have a rather correlative relationship. When PTSD and depression co-occur, this may be a manifestation of the underlying vulnerability to respond to trauma with the behavioral, affective, and cognitive symptoms reflecting the internalizing dimension. That is, people who report high levels of neuroticism are prone to react to everyday stressors and challenges with anxiety, worry, irritability, and sadness (i.e., negative affect). This style is particularly invoked when the challenge involves loss, threat, or frustration.[110]

In the late 1980s and early '90s, large-scale and comprehensive epidemiological studies of PTSD were launched.[111] In addition, the National Comorbidity Survey was initiated in 1990. This effort assessed a broad range of current and lifetime DSM-III-R diagnoses in a nationally representative sample. Kessler and colleagues reported that 47.9 percent of men and 48.5 percent of women with PTSD also had depression, consistent with the rate reported in the Detroit Area Survey of Trauma.[112,113] The rate of comorbidity in the National Comorbidity Survey-Replication, which used DSM-TV diagnostic criteria for PTSD and depression, was 42.8 percent.[114]

These ailments can certainly slow down your ACL rehabilitation. More importantly, though, they can overtake your daily life. Depression and avolition can make even the most trivial activities challenging. Using ACT to overcome these issues is paramount for an efficient experience and optimal therapeutic outcomes. The change you will notice when practicing ACT methods is that, while the feelings of sadness or lack of motivation won't magically subside, they will hold less power over you. I understand this may feel simple, and it is. Once we give in to the process and realize that we will never truly be "perfect" the way commercials or society at large say, the sooner we are able to accept these difficulties. This acceptance will allow us to start down the path of healing.

The effects that ACT had on me personally in this situation were small but profound. As Dr. Hayes depicts in many of his published works, the pivots are small, incremental changes that connect beautifully to make a "dance" that allows you to thrive in your current life. I began to notice myself making choices that were in alignment with my values.

For example, I would no longer seek out situations that would actively create chaos in my life. Instead of pushing the envelope with substances and searching for feelings, I would come to grips with my current state. I would then put my energy and effort into various components of my life that brought meaning and fulfillment, such as entrepreneurship. These small daily acts of acceptance and mindful action brought me back from a long tenure of pain and emptiness. Prioritizing my values was the pivot that bridged my broken habits and psyche to living the life I wanted.

When I finally grasped this concept, I intuitively began to use and benefit from the principles at large. The culmination of these small decisions led me from the darkest times to living a more hopeful and exciting life than ever before. Not only did my professional life benefit from this pivot, but so did my relationships. More specifically, I was finally able to build back (albeit slowly) my self-esteem and self-identity, therefore positively affecting my professional and personal life.

Chapter 15: Self-Esteem and Self-Identity

"What lies behind us and what lies before us are tiny matters compared to what lies within us."

–Ralph Waldo Emerson

At first glance, self-esteem and self-identity can seem like vastly different topics. Though, the closer you look, the more you realize that they are two sides of the same coin. As athletes, we heavily rely on our sport to define us, thinking of ourselves as "soccer players," "football players," etc.

Additionally, we also depend on our sport to increase our confidence. We all are acutely aware of how much better we feel after a good practice than a poor one, right? Dealing with our own negative thought processes is very difficult after losing the anchor of our self-esteem. The anchor for many athletes IS their sport. When that is removed, they have lost who they are and, therefore, their main source of increasing self-esteem.

Per the University of Texas at Austin's Counseling and Mental Health Center, low self-esteem is not always easy to recognize.[115] Here are three common faces that low self-esteem may wear:

The Imposter: acts happy and successful but is really terrified of failure. Lives with the constant fear that they will be found out. Needs continuous success to maintain the mask of positive self-esteem, which may lead to perfectionism, procrastination, competition, and burn-out problems.

The Rebel: acts like the opinions or goodwill of others, especially people who are important or powerful, don't matter. These individuals have tendencies to live with constant anger about not feeling good enough. Additionally, they need to prove that others' judgments and criticisms don't hurt, which may lead to problems like blaming others excessively, breaking rules or laws, or opposing authority.

The Victim: acts helpless and unable to cope with the world and waits for someone to come to the rescue. Uses self-pity or indifference as a shield against fear of taking responsibility for changing their life. Looks repeatedly to others for guidance, which can lead to problems such as unassertiveness, underachievement, and excessive reliance on others in relationships.

Low self-esteem can have substantial consequences. These include depression, increased anxiety, stress, and loneliness.[116] These symptoms can create numerous negative effects on your life, such as issues with romantic relationships, family, or friendships. Decreased academic and job performance is also associated with low self-esteem. These negative effects culminate in the increased likelihood for the affected individual to resort to drug or alcohol abuse, much like I did.[117]

Worst of all, these negative consequences themselves reinforce the negative self-image. This can take a person into a downward spiral of lower and lower self-esteem and increasingly unproductive or even actively self-destructive behavior.[118] This is especially true for ACL survivors, as they are struggling with a plethora of issues causing catastrophic changes throughout various facets of their lives.

One thing that remains constant throughout the post-ACL surgery rehabilitation is pain. While the injury itself never (in my experience) caused much pain, the pain from surgery was substantial. My self-esteem has always been quite low, and my ACL injuries only amplified this issue.

I grumbled and grunted as I awkwardly stood up from the couch. My legs tingled due to inactivity as I limped toward the bathroom. Walking with a straight leg brace on has never been (or will be) a talent of mine. I always felt more like a robot. A robot that had a part put in the wrong location.

Due to my fear of addiction, I have never been one to take pain medicine. That approach had both its perks and downfalls. One of the downfalls was that the weeks following surgery were full of physical (and mental) pain. There are few situations in life where you suffer physically and mentally simultaneously.

As I stumbled to the faucet, I did my best to avoid the mirror. Looking at myself always made my negative thoughts yell louder in the back of my head. I slowly made my way back to the couch, where I resumed perpetual inactivity. I would spend the day in a cloud of numbness masked by the television, hardly remembering what I watched. I continued this way for a while, allowing my toxic attitude, poor self-esteem, and lack of direction to poison both my personal and work life. Coming to the realization that I would never play football again, and therefore lose my self-identity as an athlete forever, was painful.

That pain showed up in every interaction or task that came my way. It was apparent in my career as I struggled to find meaning. It was apparent in my relationship that I had lost interest in long ago. Not because my partner wasn't sufficient, but because I couldn't feel anything. I tried and failed to *feel*, over and over. As the RFT framework suggests, I began to associate even positive things with the pain I felt. It was due to these associations that I felt I had no choice but to end our relationship to prevent further neglect that she did not deserve. Doing this, as you could expect, brought me even lower. The downward spiral I was already on dragged me lower and lower. I expected to hit rock bottom and *feel* something, anything. But it never happened. It got to the point where I would look around at what I was doing (or not doing) and simply be in disbelief.

It was one of those moments of disbelief that pushed me to start looking for skills, activities, or really anything that would alleviate my non-existent self-esteem and help me start to feel progress mentally.

The psychological effects of injuries on athletes have been studied extensively in sports psychology literature. Research has demonstrated that injured athletes experience mood disturbances, including anger, depression, and increased tension, as well as decreased self-esteem, as we previously discussed.[119,120,121,122,123] The emotional consequences of injury for an athlete with a strong sense of athletic identity can be devastating because their sense of self-worth depends on performance and their abilities as an athlete.[124] For example, competitive athletes were found to experience greater mood disturbances after injury than recreational athletes and were also slower to recover psychosocially.[125] In addition, collegiate athletes who had their athletic careers terminated by injury reported lower post-collegiate life satisfaction compared with those who did not sustain career-ending sports injuries.[126,127]

Multiple studies have identified improved outcomes and patient satisfaction among ACL patients with high self-efficacy. Self-efficacy refers to an individual's belief in their capacity to execute behaviors necessary to produce specific performance attainments. One study demonstrated that high postoperative self-efficacy was positively associated with higher activity levels, younger age, male gender, and Knee Injury and Osteoarthritis Outcome Score outcomes.[128,129] In another study, preoperative self-efficacy was found to significantly predict postoperative physical activity, return to sport, knee-related quality of life, and single-leg hop test one year following ACLR.[130]

These results suggest that an athlete's sense of self-efficacy can play an important role in successful rehabilitation and outcomes. Looking specifically at factors that may contribute to an injured athlete's sense of self-efficacy, the two most important determinants of self-efficacy in ACL-injured patients were patient-reported symptoms and internal locus of control.[131] I will further discuss this latter determinant in the next chapter. Patients who believed their own actions affected outcomes were more likely to have high levels of self-efficacy. Thus, the belief in self-determination and in one's ability to succeed may be positive prognostic traits that engender favorable surgical outcomes and higher rates of return to sport. Encouraging these positive traits and identifying athletes with low self-efficacy for possible psychological interventions should be an important consideration during an athlete's rehabilitation.

After an injury, self-protective changes can occur to preserve an athlete's self-esteem. Similar to defense mechanisms used to protect the ego, de-identifying with the athlete role and devaluing one's athletic identity serves to safeguard a person's sense of self when their career is threatened by injury or when rehabilitation is slower than expected.[132,133] In a study of 108 persons undergoing ACL surgery, the authors reported a significant decline in athletic identity over the twenty-four months postoperatively, with the most substantial decrease occurring between six and twelve months after surgery.[134]

It was proposed that this period represented the time in which an athlete would likely begin to return to sport; it also likely coincided with significant anxiety about attempting plays on the field. By distancing themselves from the athlete role at this crucial time, the athlete is theoretically able to self-protect against perceived failure and potential psychological devastation if pre-injury abilities are no longer present or possible. The time surrounding the return to sport may represent a fragile emotional period for athletes with high athletic identities, and counseling, training, or a referral to a sports psychologist to address these issues may be valuable.[135]

ACT can assist individuals struggling with this symptomology by building a sense of self-efficacy in the patient. Self-efficacy can be an instrumental building block to alleviating low self-esteem because it allows the individual to feel like they have some level of control over their situation. This can be especially helpful for athletes who are struggling with coming back from an injury and having to redefine themselves as someone who is not athletically inclined (at least initially). Various facets of ACT can have a significant impact, but not on the issues themselves. ACT, as I have said before, is not a magic pill. Instead, it is a mindset that can be built around your life to ensure that you can live life as the best version of yourself, no matter the setbacks, thoughts/emotions, or obstacles.

In conclusion, while an athlete's sense of self-efficacy is an important predictor of positive outcomes following ACL reconstruction, several factors can contribute to low self-efficacy. Identifying these factors and providing psychological interventions, when necessary, should be an important part of an athlete's rehabilitation. Encouraging an athlete's belief in self-determination and their ability to succeed is crucial for successful rehabilitation.

Chapter 16: Locus of Control

"You cannot control what happens to you, but you can control your attitude toward what happens to you, and in that, you will be mastering change rather than allowing it to master you."

–Brian Tracy

The locus of control (LOC) is a person's belief about the degree to which they control their own life. LOC has two dimensions: internal and external. Internal LOC refers to the degree to which people believe they can control their own lives, while external LOC refers to the degree to which people believe that they are controlled by external forces.

People with an internal LOC believe that they control their own lives and that luck, chance, or powerful others do not determine the outcomes of their lives. Rather, they believe that hard work and preparation will lead to success in life.

People with an external LOC believe that the world around them is controlled by chance, luck, powerful others, or outside forces. Individuals with a high external LOC believe that they have little control over the events in their lives, and that can lead to highly negative outcomes.

Pain, poor coping, and LOC had taken over my life. While most people focus on the primary symptoms, I believe LOC can be the most toxic to ACL patients' outcomes. Poor coping and pain may have led me (and presumably others) down the incorrect path, but LOC kept me on that path much longer than it should have.

Do you know the feeling of snapping out of a trance? For example, have you ever been driving, arrived at your destination, and had no memory of the journey itself? The feeling of being snapped back into reality is certainly uncomfortable and can be frightening. Additionally, the feeling of having not been in full control of yourself, whether on a drive or throughout your day-to-day life, can be very unsettling.

For the longest time, I felt that I wasn't truly in control of my life. I had done everything my coaches, trainers, and teammates had deemed appropriate and necessary to return from my first ACL injury. I trained tirelessly, yearning for the return to "normalcy" and to feel like I did before my injury. However, no matter what I did, my legs never felt like my own. It was like I had received a leg transplant from another person, and that leg was totally incompatible with my body. This incompatibility made movement unnatural and difficult, regardless of how much training I did.

This lack of progress led me to the poor coping, psychological distress, and depression that most individuals attribute to someone with an ACL tear. I felt that no matter what I did, I could not overcome those who "were in control." For the longest time, this affected me not only personally and emotionally, but also spiritually. I stopped praying and going to church, and I questioned God's existence overall. If there truly was a God, why would he let someone who was hardworking, diligent, and had faith succumb to such an unfortunate series of events?

From the abrupt end of my athletic career to the emotional abuse, struggle with substance abuse and frequent suicidal ideation, how could I truly believe that there was a greater power looking out for all of us? I am not naive enough to think that I was the only one struggling. I knew the world was full of struggle, pain, and anguish. This knowledge only pushed me further away from God and religion in general. While I do not want to speak about religion specifically, it is a singular part of my story that adequately illustrates how external LOC can drastically alter you in many ways, some of which you may not even have considered.

Locus of control has also been associated with outcomes after ACL surgery. A recent study found that patients who demonstrated a high internal locus of control scored higher on subjective outcome measures, including the KOOS Activities of Daily Living Scale, the KOOS Sports Activity Scale, and the International Knee Documentation Committee Subjective Knee Form.[136]

Patients with a more internal locus of control had higher scores for satisfaction, physical function, social function, mental health and vitality, and overall knee function.[137] As discussed, the internal locus of control has also been found to be an important determinant of self-efficacy, which is associated with favorable outcomes. It has also been shown to predict returning to sports twelve months after surgery.[138,139] This data suggests that patients who believe they can control their outcome may actually do so, to a certain extent.

Another study that analyzed 198 individual elite athletes who completed inventories measuring LOC, sense of coherence, and mental skills had applicable findings. The results revealed that individuals with an internal LOC and a high sense of coherence consistently displayed significantly higher scores on nine out of twelve mental skills than athletes scoring lower on the two trait inventories. Findings suggest that individuals who perceive their world to be controllable, manageable, and meaningful have more developed mental skills.[140]

Additional, comprehensive research on LOC demonstrates empirically that LOC is related to a broad range of functional outcomes. In particular, internal LOC is associated with various positive outcomes via at least three mediating processes. Overall, it appears that the personality trait of LOC provides a useful theoretical perspective to enhance our explanation and prediction of individuals' attitudes and behaviors.[141]

ACT can help individuals struggling with this symptomology by teaching them how to take control of their thoughts and feelings. This is done through various exercises and mindfulness practices that help people become more aware of their thoughts and feelings as they are happening. ACT also teaches people how to accept their thoughts and feelings, even if they are not pleasant, without judging themselves. This skill is imperative because although individuals may feel as though they aren't in control of their lives, like many thoughts, this can be cast aside. They can continue to live in the moment with those thoughts while affirming their true situation and the reality that only we are truly in control of our day-to-day lives. This can be difficult initially, but it is a practice that can be developed with time and patience.

It is evident that LOC has a tremendous impact on our lives. Whether it is our physical or mental health, LOC can dictate how we cope with difficult situations. For those who have suffered an ACL tear, it is important to understand how LOC can affect you both physically and emotionally. If you are struggling to regain your previous level of function, it is important to seek out help from a professional who can assist you in developing a more internal LOC. With hard work and dedication, those with a high internal LOC can often achieve better outcomes both physically and mentally.

Chapter 17: Kinesiophobia

"Each of us must confront our own fears, must come face to face with them. How we handle our fears will determine where we go with the rest of our lives. To experience adventure or to be limited by the fear of it."

–Judy Blume

Kinesiophobia. A jumble of letters and syllables. While it may seem like a foreign concept, it is extremely humbling and prevalent to those who have torn their ACL. This condition can be defined as:

> "A condition in which a patient has an excessive, irrational and debilitating fear of physical movement and activity resulting from a feeling of vulnerability to painful injury or **re-injury."** [142]

This condition has been a daily reminder of my ACL injury and the irrevocable damage that it (previously) did to my psyche. Even though I have done things physically over the last number of years that pre-ACL tear me would only dream of doing, I still felt I couldn't do anything remotely competitive or athletic. I refused any type of athletic activity (except lifting weights or working out), considering it to be another opportunity to tear my ACL.

"Hey! What are you up to? Do you want to go play basketball this evening with the rest of the guys? We can have some fun before we have to think about finals next week."

My anxiety skyrocketed, and my palms started to sweat. As the montage of potential ACL injuries ran through my head, I tried to quickly calculate the best way to get out of this situation. I remember feeling empty as I hung up the phone. Every single time I had to avoid something I knew deep down I wanted to do, my knee and previous injuries came to mind. I suppose that isn't an appropriate way to say it. My knee and my injuries didn't *come to mind*. They *took over* my brain.

I would picture myself doing whatever I wanted, but it would end with a small tweak, a pop, and a sudden fall. It got to the point where I wouldn't jog, run, or even dance (although, admittedly, that was rare). Luckily, I got past that milestone quickly, but it took work. I have been working through ACT and developing these principles, pivots, and skills in my daily life for over two years. Although I am not anywhere near where I want to be, I continue to move closer and closer to where I need to be for my loved ones and myself each day.

To this day, it breaks my heart to think about all of the things I have avoided due to my fear. I once heard a quote that has always stuck with me, and I think (if you're anything like me) it will also ring true to you:

> *"Twenty years from now, you will be more disappointed by the things you didn't do than by*

the ones you did. So, throw off the bowlines. Sail away from the safe harbor. Catch the trade winds in your sails. Explore. Dream. Discover."

–Mark Twain

After years of avoidance, I can regrettably inform you that this quote is 100 percent accurate. I have missed so many opportunities for various activities, and unfortunately, more than just the loss of experiences haunts me. It also bothers me that I lost the experiences because, in those instances, I am certain I could have created even stronger relationships with those around me. My impression is that experiences, or rather, time, are the greatest gift, asset, and resource we have as humans. It is with time that we can create or build whatever we want in our perspective worlds, and due to kinesiophobia, I couldn't spend my time the way I deemed fit.

In my opinion, there are a few crucial elements that are missing within the knee health industry today. Yes, there is a monumental gap in what ACL survivors *should* be doing physically, which I plan to discuss in future resources, but also how to combat kinesiophobia. This cascades into a number of the other conditions that we discussed throughout this book, because if you are actively avoiding something you want, you are likely depressed, using poor coping mechanisms, and losing your self-identity and self-esteem.

Copious amounts of research have been completed evaluating the effect kinesiophobia has on the rehabilitation outcomes of ACL patients.[143,144,145,146,147,148]

One study demonstrated that greater kinesiophobia was associated with worse outcomes after ACL surgery. The literature continued to state that interventions that improve the ability to perform knee-related activities of daily living may be appropriate to minimize the impact of fear in less active patients, while those targeting hop performance and knee-related sports activities may be better suited for more active patients.[149]

Another study found that isometric quadriceps strength and lower levels of kinesiophobia are significantly associated with positive long-term patient-reported outcomes after ACL surgery.[150] Patient-reported outcomes are generally standardized surveys that the patient completes without interpretation of the associated clinician. These surveys allow researchers to ascertain the effectiveness of the interventions from the patient's perspective.

Additional research has found that patients with greater self-reported fear were less active, presented with lower single-leg hop performance and isometric quadriceps strength, and had an increased risk of suffering a second ACL injury in the twenty-four months after returning to sport.[151]

Evidence supports an association between knee impairment, functional and psychological variables, and return to sport. Current return to sport guidelines should be updated to reflect all variables associated with returning to sports. Utilizing evidence-based return to sport guidelines following ACL surgery may ensure that athletes are physically and psychologically capable of participating in sports, which may reduce reinjury rates and the need for subsequent surgery.[152]

I dug through the literature incessantly and found many more problems than solutions, as you might expect. The literature continued to discuss the physical aspects of how to prevent kinesiophobia, and *if* they did mention anything about the psychological aspects of recovering, it was only regarding the timing of *when* kinesiophobia could be improved. I believe this gap in the healthcare continuum could be adequately addressed by ACT.

As I discussed previously, although ACT is less widely known than other behavior-based activities like CBT, it may be the appropriate intervention. The core tenets of ACT most closely align with athletics and the need to realize that only you can control your future. Rather than focusing on changing negative thoughts that you cannot control, with the therapist largely in control, you can focus on accepting that negative thoughts, feelings, emotions, memories, and behaviors are part of life.

In ACT, the control is equally divided between the therapist/coach and the patient. Further, the main goal of CBT is to eliminate the symptoms of depression or anxiety, while in ACT, eliminating the symptoms of depression and anxiety is a beneficial side effect. As I said before and will say time and time again, this is not a magic pill that will solve all of your problems. It is just my intention to ensure that you, like me, can live more optimally with the various curveballs that life will inevitably throw at you.

If I were to describe to you how ACT can help you with kinesiophobia, it would be a very political response in which I would fail to truly answer the question. Admittedly, I would be a poor politician. I prefer providing concrete answers because that is generally how I (and I am sure others) learn the most. The reason I cannot give a substantial or definitive answer is because it will look different for each and every one of you who reads this book.

For me, it looks like going to the gym and working out without fear of reinjury or pain. It looks like enjoying the mountains during the snowboarding season and the views that, in my opinion, are nearly divine. It also looks like playing basketball, jumping, and hopefully, dunking a basketball again. What using ACT will look like for you is getting back to the things you love. While it may be at a slower pace than you like, or even slightly adapted due to your activity level, I am certain we can get you closer to completing the activities that give your life meaning.

Chapter 18: Conclusion

"The future belongs to those who believe in the beauty of their dreams."

–Eleanor Roosevelt

ACL injuries are some of the most gruesome injuries that we see. They are seen almost daily throughout athletics, whether on TV or at your local high school sporting event. An abundance of research has been conducted regarding the physical exercises that can assist ACL patients in returning to their sport. Even the effect of psychological distress on ACL patients as they go through the rehabilitation process has been researched.

One aspect that researchers have yet to identify, though, is a concrete intervention that can help this particular group of people as they go through the arduous rehabilitation process. Based on the literature, my own personal experience, and the transformation I have had using ACT, I believe it is a sufficient intervention that can guide you through the various difficulties you are facing. I do not think it will be easy, but I believe the only way out of pain is through interpersonal relationships. My passion is helping those who, like me, have struggled or are struggling with the psychological components of ACL injury or knee pain.

As outlined in this book, I believe there is a solution to the psychological distress inherent with an ACL injury, which is ACT. I compared ACT to a better-known behavioral therapy, CBT. I also went over all six of the pivots that are part of ACT and how they can help you in your current situation. I described the situations that I was able to overcome using these principles and the passion I have for you personally.

We also discussed, in greater detail, an overview of the six pivots necessary to utilize ACT effectively. I described the nature of defusion, acceptance, and mindfulness. I also discussed how these three components can allow you to live a more fulfilling life, free from psychological distress. Additionally, becoming in tune with your personal values and true self while allowing these components to guide purposeful action in your life can greatly increase your psychological flexibility. Through this psychological flexibility, you will find what you are looking for, as I have, in the ACL rehabilitation process.

In conclusion, I want you to know that there is always hope. No matter how bleak your situation may seem, I believe that, with the help of ACT and the willingness to change, you can overcome any obstacle in your way, including an ACL tear.

You will likely face many challenges throughout your rehabilitation process that may seem insurmountable at first. It is important to go into this with the understanding that there will be bad days, and that is okay. What matters is that you keep pushing forward. With continued practice of psychological flexibility, you can transform your ACL injury from something that thwarts your hopes and dreams to something that strengthens them.

Lastly, I sincerely thank you for your support, and I hope that you found the beginning of your journey within the pages of this book. I would like to personally connect with you if you found meaning and hope within my book. Please visit my website for more information on how I can assist you and to discover other resources that I have that could provide value to your life.

Thank you for reading,
Keagen Hadley
The ACL Therapist
https://keagenhadley.com/

Notes

For a full list of the references contained in this book, please visit my website:

https://keagenhadley.com/.

TORN

The Mindful Athlete Workbook

How to Use ACT to Cultivate Psychological Flexibility for Peak Performance

The Mindful Athlete Workbook
Contents

Introduction

Welcome to the "Torn" workbook—a comprehensive guide that bridges the gap between physical prowess and mental resilience. This invaluable resource is tailored to athletes like you, aiming to empower you with the essential skills derived from ACT. Through the mastery of these skills, you'll not only elevate your athletic performance but also enrich your overall well-being.

In the dynamic world of sports, mental flexibility is just as crucial as physical agility. This workbook is your compass, leading you toward a heightened sense of psychological flexibility—a trait that enables you to navigate challenges, maintain unwavering focus, and excel under pressure. It is a journey that intertwines commitment and acceptance, values and purpose, mindfulness and self-awareness.

Navigating the Workbook

This workbook is organized into sections, each centered around a core psychological flexibility skill. Within each section, you'll find actionable steps, exercises, and techniques meticulously crafted to resonate with the demands of your athletic journey. As you delve into each skill, you'll uncover its relevance to your athletic pursuits and discover how it can enhance your performance, mindset, and overall athletic experience.

Your Path to Success

Embracing psychological flexibility is a journey that mirrors the training regimen you're familiar with. Just as you refine your physical abilities through consistent practice, these skills require dedicated effort and commitment. Each activity you engage in is a stepping stone toward mastering the art of psychological flexibility, offering you tools to manage thoughts, emotions, and situations more effectively.

What Lies Ahead

Throughout this workbook, you'll embark on a transformative exploration of the following psychological flexibility skills:

1. **Acceptance:** Learn to embrace your thoughts and emotions without judgment, empowering you to approach challenges with clarity and emotional balance.

2. **Defusion:** Discover techniques to distance yourself from unhelpful thoughts and gain control over their impact on your mindset.

3. **Mindfulness:** Cultivate present-moment awareness to sharpen your focus, alleviate stress, and heighten your athletic experience.

4. **Self as Context:** Develop a strong sense of self-awareness that enables you to view challenges and successes from a broader perspective.

5. **Values:** Clarify your core values and weave them into your athletic pursuits, giving you a clear sense of purpose and direction.

6. **Purposeful Action:** Harness your values to set meaningful goals and take intentional steps toward your desired outcomes.

Empower Your Athletic Journey

By embarking on this workbook, you're taking significant strides toward becoming a mindful athlete—someone who leverages psychological flexibility to excel on and off the field. Your commitment to this journey reflects your dedication to achieving peak performance while nurturing your well-being. As you engage with each section, activity, and technique, you'll unearth the transformative potential within you.

Prepare to embark on a remarkable journey of self-discovery and empowerment. The skills you cultivate within these pages will serve as steadfast companions in your athletic pursuits. Your athletic journey is about to enter a new dimension, where mental resilience and psychological agility stand as pillars of your success. Let's dive in and uncover the treasures that lie ahead.

Acceptance

In the context of ACT, "acceptance" isn't about passive resignation or tolerating undesirable circumstances. Instead, it's a powerful, proactive stance toward your thoughts, emotions, and experiences, both on and off the field.

Acceptance Means Acknowledging Reality

Acceptance starts with recognizing and acknowledging your thoughts and feelings as they are, without judgment or resistance. It's about saying, "This is what I'm experiencing right now."

Non-Struggle with Internal Experiences

It involves letting go of the struggle against your own thoughts and emotions. Instead of trying to control or suppress them, acceptance encourages you to make space for them in your awareness.

Recognizing Thoughts as Mental Events

In ACT, thoughts are seen as mental events, not facts. Acceptance helps you understand that just because you think something doesn't make it true or valid.

Why Is Acceptance Important for Athletes?

Acceptance is a game-changer for athletes for several reasons:

1. **Embracing the Full Spectrum of Emotions:** Athletes often experience a wide range of emotions—from excitement and confidence to anxiety and self-doubt. Acceptance allows you to embrace these emotions without being overwhelmed by them.

2. **Enhanced Resilience:** When you accept your thoughts and feelings, you become more resilient. You can bounce back from setbacks and stay focused, even in the face of adversity.

3. **Freedom from Mental Blocks:** Acceptance helps you break free from mental blocks that can hinder your performance. Instead of getting caught up in self-criticism or doubt, you can stay in the moment and perform at your best.

4. **Improved Decision-Making:** By acknowledging your thoughts without judgment, you can make clearer and more effective decisions, both in training and competition.

5. **Emotional Balance:** Acceptance contributes to emotional balance, allowing you to maintain composure under pressure and make rational choices.

In this workbook, you will engage in activities and exercises designed to teach you how to apply the concept of acceptance in your athletic journey. These tools will empower you to embrace your thoughts and feelings, freeing you to perform at your best while nurturing your overall well-being.

As you delve into the exercises and techniques in *The Mindful Athlete Workbook,* remember that these tools are your ally. They're your ticket to greater mental resilience, focus, and success as an athlete. Embrace them, practice them, and watch as they transform the way you approach challenges and victories both on and off the field of competition.

Activity 1: Mindful Observation of Physical Sensations

Actionable Steps

Step 1: Create a Calm Space

Find a quiet and comfortable space where you won't be interrupted. This could be a corner of your room, a park, or any place where you feel at ease. Sit down in a position that allows you to be both relaxed and attentive to your thoughts and emotions. For me, this is lying on my bed or on the floor of my living room.

Step 2: Center Yourself with Breath

Close your eyes gently and take a moment to focus on your breath. Inhale deeply through your nose, feel your abdomen rise, and exhale slowly through your mouth. Do this four times, letting go of any distractions and centering your attention. If you do notice your thoughts wandering, just acknowledge that and return to your breath, focusing on the exercise.

Step 3: Tune into Your Body

As you continue to breathe calmly, start shifting your attention to the physical sensations within your body. Begin with your feet and work your way upward, noting any sensations you encounter. You might notice the pressure of your body against the surface you're sitting on, the temperature of the air around you, or even the subtle movement of your clothing against your skin.

Step 4: Observe without Judgment

As you bring your awareness to these sensations, remind yourself that there's no need to judge or analyze them. Simply notice what you're feeling, whether it's tension, warmth, coolness, or any other sensation. It's important to approach this exercise with curiosity rather than evaluation.

Step 5: Explore Tension and Relaxation

Pay particular attention to areas where you might sense tension or discomfort. Acknowledge these sensations without trying to push them away. Similarly, notice any places in your body that feel relaxed or at ease. The goal is to observe these sensations with an open mind, accepting them as part of your present experience.

Step 6: Cultivate Acceptance

During this exercise, practice acceptance of whatever you're feeling. If you encounter discomfort or tension, remind yourself that it's okay—you're simply observing your body's responses in this moment. Avoid the urge to change or fix anything. Instead, embrace the sensations as they are, recognizing that they are temporary and ever-changing.

Step 7: Conclude Mindfully

After a few minutes of observation, slowly shift your focus back to your breath. Take a few deep breaths to recenter yourself. When you're ready, gently open your eyes. Take a moment to reflect on your experience, noting any insights or feelings that arose during the practice.

Step 8: Take Note

What has truly helped me on my journey has been keeping a journal of my exercises and my progression over time. My journal has allowed me to notice tendencies and thoroughly understand my physical and emotional self over time, and it has given me insight into what I need to focus on and where I have grown.

Tips

- If your mind starts wandering, gently guide your focus back to the sensations in your body.
- Be patient with yourself. This practice might feel unfamiliar at first, but with time, it can become a valuable tool for self-awareness and relaxation.
- You can vary the duration of this practice based on your comfort level—it could range from a few minutes to more extended periods for more advanced users.

Remember, the goal of this activity is to help you connect with the present moment and develop a greater awareness of your body's sensations. Over time, this practice can contribute to improved mindfulness and overall psychological flexibility.

Activity 2: Embracing Wisdom from Difficult Experiences

Actionable Steps

Step 1: Set the Stage

Find a quiet and comfortable place where you can reflect without distractions. Have a journal or a piece of paper and a pen ready to record your thoughts and insights.

Step 2: Recall the Difficult Situation

Close your eyes and take a few deep breaths to center yourself. Choose a specific difficult situation from your past that still lingers in your thoughts. It could be a mistake, a setback, a disappointment, or a challenging event. Allow yourself to immerse in the memory.

Step 3: Observe Your Thoughts and Feelings

As you reflect on the difficult situation, pay attention to the thoughts and emotions that arise. Are there any self-critical or negative thoughts? Notice the sensations in your body as you remember the event. Without judgment, allow these thoughts and emotions to surface.

Step 4: Identify the Lessons

Consider what you have learned from this challenging experience. What insights have you gained about yourself, others, or the situation? Think about how this experience has contributed to your personal growth and understanding. Write these lessons in your journal.

Step 5: Shift to the Present

Now, bring your attention to the present moment. Remind yourself that the difficulties you've faced have shaped your current self. Reflect on any positive changes or personal strengths that have emerged from navigating through this experience.

Step 6: Embrace Acceptance

Acknowledge that difficult experiences are a part of life and they contribute to your unique journey. Practice self-compassion by telling yourself you did the best you could with the knowledge and resources you had at that time. Allow any residual emotions to be present without resistance.

Step 7: Find the Wisdom

Imagine yourself standing at a crossroads with the wisdom you've gained from this difficult experience in your hands. Envision this wisdom as a source of light that guides your path. Recognize that you can choose to move forward with this newfound wisdom to create a brighter future.

Step 8: Set an Intention

Write a statement of intention or affirmation that encapsulates your commitment to using the lessons learned from this difficult situation to become the best version of yourself. This could be a phrase like, "I embrace my past experiences as sources of wisdom, and I use this wisdom to thrive."

Step 9: Visualize Your Future Self

Close your eyes and visualize your future self—the version of you who has integrated these lessons and wisdom into your being. Imagine this future self-confidently navigating challenges, making decisions aligned with your values, and living a fulfilling life.

Step 10: Express Gratitude

Take a moment to express gratitude for the growth and wisdom that have come from your difficult experiences. Even though these moments were challenging, they have contributed to your resilience and personal development.

Step 11: Reflect and Journal

Open your eyes and reflect on the experience. Write in your journal about your insights, the wisdom you've embraced, and how you envision applying this wisdom moving forward. Consider how this practice aligns with the principles of ACT.

Tips

- Be patient with yourself as you reflect on difficult experiences. It's natural to experience a range of emotions during this process.

- This activity is about finding meaning and growth in challenging situations. Avoid placing blame on yourself or others.
- Remember that acknowledging and accepting your past experiences is a step toward psychological flexibility and personal growth.

By engaging in this activity, you're cultivating psychological flexibility through acceptance and the integration of wisdom from difficult situations. This process empowers you to move forward with purpose and authenticity, embracing your journey and becoming the best version of yourself.

Defusion

In the world of ACT, "defusion" is a concept that invites you to untangle yourself from your thoughts. It's the process of creating distance between you and your thinking patterns, allowing you to view your thoughts as mental events rather than absolute truths. Defusion is all about saying, "I am not my thoughts; I have thoughts."

Key Aspects of Defusion

1. **Observing Thoughts:** Defusion involves observing your thoughts from a detached perspective, as if you were an impartial observer. It's about becoming curious about your thought patterns.
2. **Naming Thoughts:** You may give your thoughts labels like "I'm having the thought that…" or "My mind is saying…" This helps you create a separation between yourself and your thoughts.
3. **Playful Interaction:** In ACT, there's a playful element to defusion. It encourages you to engage with your thoughts in a lighthearted manner, understanding that thoughts are just mental events, not definitive statements about reality.

Activity 3: Thought-Labeling and Thanking

Actionable Steps

Step 1: Cultivate Mindful Awareness

Start by cultivating mindful awareness throughout your day. Whenever you notice your thoughts drifting toward self-criticism or distractions, gently redirect your attention to the present moment. This heightened awareness sets the stage for the following steps.

Step 2: Identify Self-Critical or Distracting Thoughts

Be attentive to the thoughts that arise in your mind. These could be thoughts that doubt your abilities, criticize your appearance, or create unnecessary worries. Recognize when these thoughts emerge and acknowledge that they are simply thoughts and not objective truths.

Step 3: Label the Thought

When you catch a self-critical or distracting thought, mentally label it with a neutral and descriptive phrase. For example, if the thought is "I'll never be good enough," label it as "I'm having the thought that I'll never be good enough."

Step 4: Playful Gratitude

Shift your perspective by thanking your mind for producing the thought. Use a playful and lighthearted tone, as if you're thanking a friend for sharing an interesting story. For instance, say, "Thanks, mind, for that creative thought!" This shifts the tone from judgment to curiosity. It often helps also to name your mind, especially if you are prone, like me, to negative thoughts. For reference, I have named my mind "Beau."

Step 5: Recognize the Nature of Thoughts

Reflect on the nature of thoughts as passing mental events. Understand that thoughts are not fixed or unchangeable; they come and go like clouds in the sky. By acknowledging this impermanence, you're defusing the thought's power to define your reality.

Step 6: Repeat the Process

Throughout the day, continue to notice self-critical or distracting thoughts, label them, and express gratitude to your mind. With practice, this process becomes more intuitive, and you'll find yourself automatically distancing from these thoughts.

Tips

- Don't worry if you find it challenging to catch every thought. The goal is gradual progress in becoming more aware of your thinking patterns. Like any other "exercise," it will take practice to become proficient in this skill. Start with trying to complete this activity for 5 minutes a day, then slowly progress. You will notice it becomes more natural the longer you practice.

- Approach the thought-labeling and thanking process with curiosity and an open mind. The aim is to observe, not judge.
- Experiment with different playful ways of thanking your mind. You can use humor or mimic the tone you'd use with a close friend.

Additional Practice

- If you find it helpful, keep a thought journal. Write down self-critical or distracting thoughts you notice during the day, along with the labels and playful gratitudes you come up with.
- Share this activity with a friend or loved one and engage in a lighthearted conversation about the humorous and creative ways you're thanking your mind for producing these thoughts.

By engaging in thought-labeling and playful gratitude, you're learning to defuse the influence of self-critical or distracting thoughts. This skill empowers you to see your thoughts as fleeting mental events, ultimately reducing their impact on your emotions and actions. Over time, you'll become more adept at approaching your thoughts with curiosity and detachment.

Activity 4: Thought Repetition and Changing Perspective

Actionable Steps

Step 1: Select a Self-Doubtful Thought

Choose a self-doubtful thought that tends to creep in before your performances. It could be something like "I won't perform well" or "I'll mess up under pressure." Select a thought that you've noticed has a negative impact on your confidence and focus.

Step 2: Set the Stage

Find a quiet and comfortable spot where you won't be disturbed. Whether you're standing or sitting, ensure you're in a posture that allows you to feel present and focused.

Step 3: Repeat the Thought

Start by taking a deep breath to center yourself. Then, repeat the self-doubtful thought either out loud or silently in your mind. Allow the thought to flow naturally, and don't judge it or resist it.

Step 4: Adjust the Speed and Pitch

As you repeat the thought, experiment with its speed and pitch. Gradually speed up the repetition as if you're fast-forwarding through it. Alternatively, try altering the pitch—make it higher or lower. Observe how these adjustments affect the way the thought resonates within you.

Step 5: Observe the Diminishing Impact

Keep repeating the thought while manipulating its speed and pitch. Notice how, over time, the thought loses its grip on your emotions. You might sense its power over you is diminishing.

Step 6: Adopt a Cartoon Character's Perspective

Now, take a creative leap. Imagine the self-doubtful thought being spoken by a cartoon character—one that's known for its quirky voice and personality. Visualize this character, embodying the thought in a humorous and exaggerated manner.

Step 7: Reflect and Observe

As you wrap up the exercise, take a moment to reflect on your experience. How has the thought transformed as you altered its characteristics? How does it feel different now compared to when you began? Note any shifts in your emotional response.

Tips

- Approach this activity with curiosity and a sense of playfulness. The goal is to experiment with the malleability of thoughts.

- Don't worry if it feels a bit awkward at first. With practice, you'll become more comfortable altering your thought patterns.

- Remember that the purpose is to defuse the thought's negative impact. You're exploring how shifting your perspective can reshape your relationship with the thought.

Additional Practice

- Incorporate this exercise into your pre-performance routine. As you gear up for a competition, engage in this activity to defuse self-doubt and build a confident mindset.

- Share this activity with your fellow athletes. Organize a session where you collectively explore altering and reframing each other's self-doubtful thoughts. This can create a supportive atmosphere and encourage creative thinking.

By participating in thought repetition and changing perspective, you're actively defusing the influence of self-doubtful thoughts. This playful approach empowers you to witness the transformation of these thoughts and their decreasing impact on your emotions and performance. As you continue practicing, you'll develop a valuable skill that contributes to psychological flexibility, bolstering your mindset for success in sports and beyond.

Mindfulness

Mindfulness, within the context of ACT, is more than a buzzword; it's a way of being, a state of heightened awareness. It's about being fully present in the here and now, with an open and non-judgmental attitude toward your experiences. Mindfulness is the art of saying, "I am here, in this moment, without judgment."

Core Aspects of Mindfulness

1. **Present-Moment Awareness:** Mindfulness involves paying deliberate attention to the present moment, including your thoughts, sensations, emotions, and the environment around you.

2. **Non-Judgmental Observation:** It encourages you to observe these experiences without evaluating them as good or bad, right or wrong. It's about accepting the moment as it is.

3. **Open Curiosity:** Mindfulness fosters a sense of curiosity and receptivity, inviting you to explore your inner and outer worlds with a fresh perspective.

Why Is Mindfulness Important for Athletes?

Mindfulness holds immense value for athletes in numerous ways:

1. **Heightened Focus:** Mindfulness enhances your ability to concentrate and stay in the zone during training and competition, helping you make split-second decisions and perform at your best.

2. **Stress Reduction:** It equips you with tools to manage stress effectively, reducing the mental clutter that can hinder your performance.

3. **Emotional Regulation:** Mindfulness helps you recognize and regulate your emotions, preventing them from getting in the way of your goals.

4. **Enhanced Self-Awareness:** It deepens your understanding of yourself, enabling you to identify strengths, weaknesses, and areas for growth.

5. **Overall Well-Being:** Beyond athletics, mindfulness contributes to your general well-being by reducing anxiety, improving sleep, and enhancing overall life satisfaction.

Activity 5: Breath Awareness and Body Scan

Actionable Steps

Step 1: Create a Serene Space

Begin by finding a tranquil environment where you can immerse yourself in this practice. Choose a spot where you can sit or lie down without interruptions. Make sure you're comfortable and supported.

Step 2: Settle into Comfort

Close your eyes gently and assume a comfortable position. Whether you're sitting with a straight back or lying down, ensure that you're relaxed yet alert. This allows you to be fully present for the practice.

Step 3: Turn Your Focus Inward

Direct your attention to your breath. Feel the gentle rhythm of your inhalations and exhalations. Observe the rise and fall of your chest or the movement of your abdomen as you breathe.

Step 4: Immerse in the Sensation

Deepen your awareness of each breath. Notice the coolness of the air as you inhale and the warmth as you exhale. Anchor your attention to this sensation, using your breath as an anchor for the present moment.

Step 5: Begin the Body Scan

Shift your attention from your breath to different parts of your body. Start with your toes and gradually move upwards, segment by segment. You might go from your toes to your feet, ankles, calves, and so on.

Step 6: Observe Sensations without Judgment

As you focus on each body part, observe any sensations you encounter. These could range from warmth and relaxation to areas of tension. Approach these sensations without judgment; there's no need to label them as good or bad.

Step 7: Allow Sensations to Exist

Allow the sensations simply to exist. If you come across tension, discomfort, or even areas of ease, let them be as they are. The aim is to observe without the need to change or fix anything.

Step 8: Conclude the Body Scan

Once you've explored each part of your body, take a few moments to return to your breath. Let your attention rest on your breath for a few cycles, gently bringing your awareness back from the body scan.

Tips

- If your mind starts wandering, gently guide your focus back to your breath or the body part you're scanning.

- As you observe sensations, avoid trying to analyze them. Instead, adopt a curious and open mindset.

Additional Practice

- Extend the body scan by spending extra time on areas that feel particularly tense or relaxed. Imagine sending your breath to these areas, fostering a sense of release.
- Incorporate this practice into your daily routine. Engage in a brief breath awareness and body scan session in the morning or before bed to promote relaxation and mindfulness.

By participating in breath awareness and a body scan, you're cultivating a profound sense of mindfulness and self-awareness. This practice empowers you to be fully present in your body, releasing tension and fostering a deeper connection with yourself. Over time, this skill contributes to your psychological flexibility, enhancing your ability to handle challenges and perform at your best.

Activity 6: Mindful Performance Reflection

Actionable Steps

Step 1: Set Aside Time for Reflection

Allocate a few minutes after a training session or competition for mindful reflection. Find a quiet space where you can sit comfortably without interruptions.

Step 2: Create a Reflective Atmosphere

Close your eyes gently and take a few deep breaths to center yourself. Allow any tension to dissolve, creating a space of calm presence.

Step 3: Recall the Experience

Begin by bringing the training session or competition to mind. Imagine it unfolding like a movie scene. Don't focus on evaluating the experience; instead, aim to replay it as if you're an observer.

Step 4: Tune into Your Inner Landscape

As you recall the experience, pay attention to your internal world. Notice the thoughts that arise, the emotions you felt, and the physical sensations in your body. Be an impartial witness to these aspects.

Step 5: Non-Judgmental Observation

As thoughts surface, practice non-judgmental observation. If self-critical or evaluative thoughts emerge, don't engage with them. Allow them to pass like clouds in the sky.

Step 6: Cultivate Curiosity

Approach this reflection with curiosity. Instead of seeking answers or solutions, inquire about your mental state during the performance. Were you calm, anxious, focused, or distracted? Observe without criticism.

Step 7: Embrace All Aspects

Acknowledge the entirety of your experience, both the positive and challenging aspects. Allow space for any emotions that arise—pride, disappointment, excitement, or frustration.

Step 8: Take Insights Forward

As you conclude the reflection, take note of any insights that emerged. Did you notice patterns in your thinking? Were there moments when your focus wavered? These observations provide valuable information.

Step 9: Prepare for Future Performances

Use these insights to prepare for future training sessions or competitions. Consider how you can leverage your strengths and address any areas that need attention. Approach this planning with a growth mindset.

Tips

- If strong emotions arise during the reflection, take a deep breath and anchor yourself in the present moment.
- Avoid self-criticism; the goal is to learn and grow from your experiences.
- Reflect regularly to build a habit of mindfulness and self-awareness.

Additional Practice

- Keep a reflection journal to record your insights after each training session or competition. Over time, you'll accumulate a valuable resource for self-improvement.
- Share your reflective practice with a coach or mentor. Their input can provide additional perspectives and support your growth.

By engaging in mindful performance reflection, you're nurturing self-awareness and psychological flexibility. This practice empowers you to observe your experiences without judgment, gain valuable insights, and use these insights to refine your approach in future performances. With consistent reflection, you're cultivating a deeper understanding of your mental state and harnessing the power of self-awareness for optimal athletic performance.

In today's world, it is common for us to scroll mindlessly and live in the past or future, but as an athlete, that isn't conducive to our goals. Living in the moment isn't only the healthiest way to live, but also it can help us take action and work toward our goals. Each day is a new opportunity for us to take a baby step toward the athlete and person we want to be, and we cannot take that step unless we are living in the present.

Self as Context

In our daily lives, we often inhabit two distinct versions of ourselves: the "true self" and the "perceived self." These two facets of our identity play a profound role in shaping our experiences, especially in the world of sports.

1. **The True Self:** This is your core identity, the unadulterated essence of who you are. It encompasses your values, passions, and unfiltered authenticity. Your true self is the compass that points toward your most authentic desires and aspirations, as well as your limits and shortcomings.

2. **The Perceived Self:** Think of this as the external persona you project to the world. It's the version of yourself that may be influenced by societal expectations, peer pressure, or the desire to conform to a certain image. The perceived self can sometimes obscure your true essence.

Why Self as Context Matters for Athletes

Now, you might wonder, "Why is this relevant to athletes?"

1. **Alignment with Purpose:** Embracing your true self allows you to align your athletic journey with your core values and passions. When your actions

resonate with your authentic self, your sense of purpose and motivation soar.

2. **Resilience Through Authenticity:** Authenticity is a wellspring of resilience. Athletes who connect with their true selves tend to weather the storms of competition and adversity with greater grace and fortitude, because they understand their weaknesses and are better able to improve upon them.

3. **Peak Performance Zone:** Recognizing the interplay between your true self and your perceived self can propel you into the elusive "zone" where performance flows effortlessly. When your actions align with your authentic desires, extraordinary achievements become possible.

Practical Application for Athletes

Throughout this workbook, you will actively participate in exercises and activities aimed at helping you uncover your true self while acknowledging the role of your perceived self. These practical tools empower you to stride confidently toward your athletic goals with authenticity as your guiding star.

As you navigate this journey, remember that self as context invites you to strip away the layers of external expectations and rediscover your innermost desires. By embracing your true self, you'll tap into a wellspring of motivation, resilience, and peak performance.

Activity 7: Observer-Self Visualization

Actionable Steps

Step 1: Set the Scene for Visualization

Find a quiet and comfortable place to sit. Close your eyes gently, allowing yourself to relax into a peaceful state. Take a few deep breaths to ground yourself in the present moment.

Step 2: Cultivate the Observer's Perspective

Imagine yourself stepping outside of your own body, as if you're a separate observer. Visualize watching yourself—your actions, thoughts, and emotions—from a slightly elevated or detached vantage point.

Step 3: Create the Observer Self

As you assume this "observer" perspective, envision yourself as a wise and compassionate version of you. Picture this version of yourself radiating a sense of calm, understanding, and non-judgment.

Step 4: Observe Your Experiences

From this observer-self perspective, direct your attention to your actions and thoughts. Observe them with gentle curiosity, as if you're watching a movie unfold. Notice any emotions that arise.

Step 5: Embrace Compassionate Observation

As you continue to observe, infuse your visualization with compassion. Imagine that your observer self is sending understanding and warmth toward your experiences, regardless of their nature.

Step 6: Witness the Shift in Relationship

Observe how this perspective changes your relationship with your experiences. Notice if you're able to view your thoughts and actions with greater objectivity and understanding.

Step 7: Cultivate the Understanding

Take a moment to remind yourself that you are more than your thoughts and actions. Embrace the understanding that you can observe and engage with your experiences without being defined by them.

Step 8: Conclude the Visualization

Slowly bring your attention back to the present moment. Gently open your eyes and take a few deep breaths. Allow the insights and feelings from the visualization to accompany you.

Tips

- If distractions arise during the visualization, gently guide your focus back to the imagery you're creating.
- Approach this visualization with an open heart and a non-judgmental attitude.

Additional Practice

- Use this visualization before a performance or challenging situation. Let your observer self provide a comforting presence to accompany you.
- Share this practice with your teammates or training partners. Engage in a discussion about how adopting an observer's perspective can impact your collective mindset and approach.

By engaging in observer-self visualization, you're cultivating a powerful tool for psychological flexibility. This practice allows you to step back from your experiences and view them with a compassionate detachment. Through this perspective, you're nurturing a healthier relationship with your thoughts, emotions, and actions. Over time, this skill enhances your ability to navigate challenges with clarity and resilience, ultimately contributing to your growth as an athlete and an individual.

Activity 8: Letter to Your Athlete Self

Actionable Steps

Step 1: Set the Tone

Find a quiet and comfortable space where you can focus on writing. Have a journal, notebook, or a blank sheet of paper ready. Create an environment that feels inviting and conducive to reflection.

Step 2: Tap into Your Encouraging Voice

Imagine yourself as an encouraging coach or mentor. Cultivate a compassionate and supportive tone that you would use to uplift a teammate or a mentee.

Step 3: Address Challenges and Setbacks

Begin your letter by acknowledging the challenges and setbacks you've faced in your athletic journey. Reflect on the times when things didn't go as planned and the moments of struggle.

Step 4: Celebrate Achievements

Emphasize the achievements and milestones you've reached along the way. Highlight the dedication, hard work, and progress you've made. Celebrate even the small victories.

Step 5: Cultivate Self-Compassion

Infuse your letter with self-compassion. Remind yourself that setbacks are a natural part of growth and that they don't define your worth. Offer words of understanding and kindness.

Step 6: Remind Yourself of Your Strengths

List your strengths and qualities as an athlete. Recognize your resilience, determination, discipline, and any unique skills you possess. Reinforce your belief in your capabilities.

Step 7: Read the Letter for Inspiration

Once you've written your letter, read it to yourself. Imagine that you're receiving these words from a caring coach or mentor. Let the words sink in and resonate with you.

Step 8: Internalize the Supportive Perspective

As you read the letter, internalize the supportive voice and perspective you've created. Imagine carrying this encouragement with you, especially during challenging times.

Step 9: Keep the Letter Accessible

Keep the letter in a place where you can easily access it. When you need a boost of confidence, motivation, or a reminder of your strengths, revisit the letter.

Tips

- Don't worry about writing perfectly; focus on expressing genuine support and kindness.
- Write as if you're speaking directly to yourself, using first-person pronouns ("you" and "your").
- Customize the letter to align with your personal experiences and journey.

Additional Practice

- Write a series of letters to your athlete self, each focusing on a different aspect of your athletic journey (e.g., preparation, competition, recovery).
- Share this activity with a fellow athlete. Exchange letters with each other, providing a unique form of support and encouragement.

By engaging in the letter-writing exercise, you're nurturing self-compassion, resilience, and a positive self-perception. This practice allows you to be your own biggest supporter and source of motivation. As you read and internalize the words of encouragement, you're tapping into a wellspring of strength that can propel you forward in your athletic pursuits. Over time, this practice contributes to your psychological flexibility and enhances your ability to navigate challenges with self-assuredness and grace.

Values

Values are fundamental principles that define what truly matters to you in life. They are the compass that guides your actions, both on and off the field, while your goals are the stepping stones in the chosen direction. In this workbook, we'll explore the significance of values within ACT and how they can profoundly impact your athletic journey.

Key Aspects of Values

1. **Personal and Unique:** Your values are deeply personal and unique to you. They reflect your authentic desires and aspirations, not external expectations or societal norms.

2. **Enduring and Motivating:** Values are enduring; they remain constantly changing throughout your life. They provide motivation and a sense of purpose, especially during challenging times.

3. **Action-Oriented:** Values are not abstract concepts; they are meant to be lived. When you align your actions with your values, you experience a profound sense of fulfillment and authenticity.

Why Values Matter for Athletes

Values play a crucial role in the athletic world:

1. **Clarity in Decision-Making:** Values offer clarity when you're faced with decisions related to training, competition, and life outside sports. They help you make choices that resonate with your true self.

2. **Motivation and Resilience:** Athletes who connect their actions to their values often find deeper motivation and resilience. Your values can be a powerful driving force during challenging moments.

3. **Enhanced Focus:** Values serve as a powerful focal point. They help you concentrate on what truly matters, reducing distractions and mental clutter that can hinder your performance. Whenever you are given a choice, it is a comfort to be able to ask, "Which path will lead me closer to my values?"

4. **Greater Satisfaction:** One thing I learned very quickly is that even if you are accomplishing your goals, it is meaningless unless you can effectively attach those results to your underlying values.

Activity 9: Values Clarification and Visualization

Actionable Steps

Step 1: Allocate Reflective Time

Set aside a dedicated period for introspection and reflection. Find a calm and quiet environment where you can delve into your thoughts without disturbances.

Step 2: Identify Your Core Values

Reflect on what deeply matters to you as an athlete. These are the values guiding your actions and decisions. Write a list of core values that resonate with you (e.g., dedication, resilience, teamwork).

Step 3: Delve into Each Value

For each value you've identified, take a moment to explore what it means to you. How does this value manifest in your athletic journey? How does it influence your actions and interactions?

Step 4: Visualize Your Values in Action

Close your eyes and enter a state of calm. Visualize yourself embodying each value in practice and competition. Imagine scenarios where you're displaying dedication, resilience, teamwork, and other values you've listed.

Step 5: Immerse Yourself in the Visualization

Dive deep into your visualization. Engage all your senses as you see, hear, and feel the embodiment of these values. Visualize yourself fully engaged and aligned with what truly matters to you.

Step 6: Connect with Your Deeper Purpose

As you continue visualizing, feel a connection with a deeper sense of purpose and motivation. Notice how embodying these values brings a heightened sense of fulfillment and meaning to your athletic journey.

Step 7: Conclude the Visualization

Slowly transition out of the visualization. Take a few deep breaths and open your eyes. Take a moment to reflect on the emotions and sensations you experienced during the practice.

Tips

- Be open to adjusting your list of values over time as you gain more clarity about what resonates with you.
- When visualizing, don't focus on perfection. Instead, embrace the process of aligning your actions with your values.

Additional Practice

- Create a vision board or visual representation of your core values and their embodiment in your athletic pursuits. Place it somewhere you can see it regularly.
- Share your values exploration with a fellow athlete. Discuss how your values influence your mindset and actions, fostering a deeper connection with your sport.

By engaging in values clarification and visualization, you're strengthening your connection with your authentic self and your athletic journey. This practice empowers you to align your actions with what truly matters to you, fostering a sense of purpose and motivation. Through visualization, you're creating a vivid picture of yourself embodying your values, which enhances your psychological flexibility and emotional resilience. Over time, this practice contributes to a more meaningful and fulfilling athletic experience.

Activity 10: Values-Based Goal-Setting

Actionable Steps

Step 1: Identify the Area for Improvement

Begin by selecting a specific aspect of your athletic performance you want to enhance. It could be related to your endurance, technique, mental resilience, teamwork, or any other relevant area.

Step 2: Craft a SMART Goal

Formulate a goal that aligns with your chosen area of improvement and your core values. Make it SMART—Specific, Measurable, Achievable, Relevant, and Time-bound. For instance, "Run a personal best in the next 5K race."

Step 3: Break Down the Goal

Divide your SMART goal into smaller, manageable steps. Create a roadmap that outlines the actions you need to take to reach your objective. Assign deadlines to each step to keep yourself accountable.

Step 4: Create an Action Plan

Develop a detailed action plan for each step. Determine what resources you need, the practice required, and the support you might seek. Consider potential obstacles and how you'll overcome them.

Step 5: Infuse Your Goal with Values

Reflect on how your goal aligns with your core values. Consider how achieving this goal will reflect your dedication, resilience, teamwork, or any other value that's important to you.

Step 6: Regularly Review and Remind Yourself

Set regular intervals for reviewing your goal and the progress you've made. Keep the goal visible—write it down, create a vision board, or use digital tools to remind yourself.

Step 7: Embrace the Journey

Understand that the pursuit of your goal is a journey, and setbacks or detours are part of the process. Approach challenges with resilience and adapt your plan as needed.

Step 8: Celebrate Milestones

As you achieve milestones on your journey, take a moment to celebrate your progress. Acknowledge the effort you've put in and the growth you've experienced.

Tips

- Choose a goal that excites you and ignites your passion for improvement.
- Be realistic in setting your goal, considering your current skill level and available resources.
- Make your action plan actionable and detailed, including specific tasks and deadlines.

Additional Practice

- Share your goal with a friend, coach, or teammate who can provide support and accountability.
- Incorporate mindfulness and reflection into your goal-setting process. Regularly pause to assess your alignment with your values and your commitment to the journey.

By engaging in values-based goal-setting, you're not only advancing your athletic performance but also deepening your connection with your values. This practice empowers you to align your aspirations with what matters most to you, fostering a sense of purpose and motivation. As you break down your goal into actionable steps, you're enhancing your psychological flexibility by building a structured pathway to achievement. Over time, this approach leads to both athletic success and personal growth.

Purposeful Action

In the dynamic world of sports, there is a fundamental principle that serves as the linchpin for profound change: purposeful action. Rooted in the core tenets of ACT, it holds the power to unlock your full potential as an athlete.

Unpacking the Essence of Purposeful Action

At its essence, purposeful action is more than mere movement; it's the deliberate and conscious steps you take. Without this skill, the rest of your progress is for naught. It's about the action you take after you have aligned your every move with your core values and authentic self. In simpler terms, it's the driving force that propels you forward, transforming not just your athletic performance but your entire life.

Activity 11: Commitment Ritual

Actionable Steps

Step 1: Reflect on Your Commitment

Spend time contemplating your unwavering dedication to your athletic journey. Revisit the reasons you started, the goals you set, and the values that fuel your passion.

Step 2: Create a Personal Ritual

Develop a unique ritual that resonates with you. Consider the following examples as inspiration:

- **Pre-Performance Mantra:** Craft a mantra that encapsulates your commitment. For instance, "I am dedicated, I am focused, I am resilient."
- **Symbolic Gesture:** Invent a gesture that symbolizes your commitment. It could be as simple as touching your heart or forming a fist before training.
- **Visualization:** Envision a scene where you're embodying your dedication. Picture yourself conquering challenges and celebrating successes.

Step 3: Craft Your Mantra or Visualization

If you're creating a mantra, choose words that motivate and empower you. Align the phrasing with your values and aspirations. If you opt for visualization, imagine every detail vividly.

Step 4: Practice Consistently

Integrate your ritual into your daily routine. Before every training session or competition, allocate a moment to engage in your chosen practice. Find a quiet space and focus your attention.

Step 5: Engage with Intention

Approach your ritual with intention and presence. Whether you're reciting your mantra, performing your gesture, or visualizing, immerse yourself fully in the experience.

Step 6: Connect with Your Purpose

Use your ritual as a conduit to reconnect with your purpose and values. As you engage with it, let the significance of your commitment flow through you.

Step 7: Reinforce Your Mindset

Allow your commitment ritual to shift your mindset. Let it be a trigger that propels you into a determined and focused state. Channel the energy it provides.

Step 8: Embrace the Experience

Embrace the sensory and emotional experience of your ritual. Relish in the motivation, strength, and sense of purpose it invokes.

Tips

- Personalize your ritual to reflect your individual preferences and beliefs.
- Keep your ritual concise and easy to integrate into your routine.

Additional Practice

- Experiment with different elements to find what resonates best with you.
- Share your ritual with a close friend or teammate. Discuss your experiences and encourage each other's commitment journeys.

By engaging in a commitment ritual tailored to your preferences, you're nurturing a profound connection with your dedication and values. This practice empowers you to infuse purpose into each training session or competition. Through consistent engagement, your chosen ritual becomes an anchor, fostering psychological flexibility and enhancing your ability to navigate challenges with unwavering determination. Ultimately, this ritual becomes a treasured tool for embracing your athletic journey fully.

Activity 12: The Power of "AND"

Actionable Steps

Step 1: Recognize Competing Thoughts and Emotions

Begin by identifying situations where you often find yourself experiencing conflicting thoughts or emotions. For instance, you might feel a mix of nervousness and excitement before a game or a competition.

Step 2: Embrace the "AND" Perspective

Embrace the concept of "AND." This means acknowledging and accepting that you can experience multiple thoughts or emotions simultaneously without favoring one over the other.

Step 3: Allow Coexistence of Emotions

Remind yourself that it's perfectly valid to be nervous AND excited, stressed AND confident. Let go of the need to categorize these feelings as mutually exclusive.

Step 4: Observe without Judgment

When these conflicting thoughts or emotions arise, practice observing them without judgment. Let go of the urge to label one feeling as right and the other as wrong.

Step 5: Embrace Acceptance

Cultivate an attitude of acceptance toward your internal experiences. Acknowledge that the coexistence of feelings is a natural part of being human.

Step 6: Take Purposeful Action

Despite feeling conflicting emotions, use the power of "AND" to move forward with purposeful action. Let the presence of discomfort motivate you rather than hold you back.

Step 7: Practice Self-Compassion

If you find yourself leaning toward self-criticism or frustration due to these conflicting feelings, apply self-compassion. Treat yourself with the same kindness you would offer to a friend.

Tips

- Be patient with yourself as you adapt to the “AND” perspective. It might feel unfamiliar at first, but it gets easier with practice.
- Don’t aim to eliminate or suppress any emotions; instead, focus on coexisting with them.

Additional Practice

- Journal about your experiences when applying the “AND” perspective. Reflect on how this approach affected your mindset and actions.
- Share the concept of “AND” with your teammates or fellow athletes. Discuss how embracing this perspective might influence your collective approach to challenges.

By engaging in the practice of “AND,” you’re fostering a powerful sense of psychological flexibility. This approach allows you to hold conflicting thoughts and emotions without feeling compelled to choose one over the other.

As you learn to accept and coexist with your internal experiences, you're cultivating a mindset that's more adaptable and resilient. Over time, this practice enables you to navigate challenges with a sense of purpose and confidence, regardless of the discomfort that might arise.

Conclusion

Congratulations on completing *The Mindful Athlete Workbook!* You've embarked on a journey that goes beyond physical prowess, one that delves into the realm of psychological flexibility and mental resilience. By integrating these fundamental skills from ACT into your training and performances, you've taken a significant step toward unlocking your full athletic potential.

Practical Integration

The psychological flexibility skills you've explored—acceptance, defusion, mindfulness, self as context, values, and purposeful action—are not just abstract concepts. They are tools designed to support you in real-life situations that athletes often encounter:

- **Pre-Competition Nerves:** When the mixture of excitement and nervousness arises before a game, employing the "AND" perspective can help you accept both emotions, allowing you to perform with heightened focus and energy.
- **Performance Setbacks:** Following a less-than-ideal performance, utilizing self-compassion and thought defusion can help you manage self-criticism, learn from the experience, and move forward stronger than before.
- **Balancing Training and Recovery:** Amid rigorous training, mindfulness can assist you in

staying present, appreciating each moment, and preventing burnout.

- **Defining Your Purpose:** During moments of doubt, connecting with your values and purpose can reignite your passion and provide a clear direction, motivating you to persevere.

Benefits to the Athlete

By incorporating these psychological flexibility skills into your athletic journey, you're opening doors to numerous benefits:

- **Mental Resilience:** You'll develop the ability to bounce back from setbacks, handle stress more effectively, and maintain a composed mindset, even in challenging situations.

- **Focused Performance:** These skills will sharpen your ability to stay focused on the present moment, freeing you from distractions and enabling peak performance.

- **Emotional Regulation:** You'll gain tools to manage your emotions, preventing them from interfering with your goals and allowing you to channel them constructively.

- **Enhanced Well-Being:** As you embrace acceptance and mindfulness, you'll nurture your overall well-being, experiencing a sense of balance and tranquility.

Diligent Practice for Mastery

Just as you dedicated countless hours to honing your athletic skills, these psychological flexibility skills also require diligent practice. Becoming proficient in these techniques is akin to becoming proficient in your sport—it takes time, patience, and continuous effort. Much like perfecting a technique or improving your stamina, these skills will become second nature with consistent practice. As you persist in engaging with the activities, techniques, and concepts outlined in this workbook, you'll witness gradual transformation.

Best of Luck on Your Athletic Journey

As you carry forward the insights and practices from this workbook, remember that you possess the tools to enhance not only your athletic performance but also your personal growth and well-being. Embrace the challenges and opportunities that lie ahead with the same dedication and enthusiasm you bring to your sport. Your journey as a mindful athlete has just begun, and with the power of psychological flexibility by your side, the possibilities are limitless. Best of luck on your athletic journey—may it be filled with growth, achievement, and profound satisfaction.

Thank You For Reading *Torn!*

I look forward to helping you in your recovery journey; go to https://keagenhadley.com/ and subscribe so that you are in the know for all future content.

Feedback is always welcome! Has my book helped you in your ACL recovery journey? Let me know by leaving me an honest review on Amazon. I need your input to make the next version of this book and future books even better.

Thanks so much!

Want to Connect?

Email: theACLtherapist@gmail.com
Facebook:facebook.com/TheACLTherapist
Twitter: @theACLtherapist
Instagram: @theACLtherapist

Keagen Hadley, OTD, OTR/L
The ACL Therapist

https://keagenhadley.com/

NOW IT'S YOUR TURN

Discover the EXACT 3-step blueprint you need to become a bestselling author in as little as 3 months.

Self-Publishing School helped me, and now I want them to help you with this FREE resource to begin outlining your book!

Even if you're busy, bad at writing, or don't know where to start, you CAN write a bestseller and build your best life.

With tools and experience across a variety of niches and professions, Self-Publishing School is the only resource you need to take your book to the finish line!

DON'T WAIT

Say "YES" to becoming a bestseller:

https://self-publishingschool.com/friend/

Follow the steps on the page to get a FREE resource to get started on your book and unlock a discount to get started with Self-Publishing School.

Acknowledgments

First and foremost, I would like to thank my family for their unconditional love and support. My friends have also been a great source of strength and encouragement, and I am truly blessed to have them in my life. Additionally, I want to express my deepest gratitude to my wife for her patience and understanding. She has been an amazing partner, and I am so lucky to have her by my side. Thank you all for being a part of my life. I am truly grateful.

Lastly, I want to thank my readers and clients. I commend you for your resiliency, strength, and willingness to take this tiny step with me in the right direction. I can't wait to hear more about your journey and successes as we work together.

ABOUT THE AUTHOR

Keagen Hadley is an occupational therapy doctor specializing in using psychological treatments such as acceptance and commitment therapy (ACT) with his patients.

As a patient and therapist, he has a deep understanding of the interventions and knows how emotional stress can interfere with rehabilitation, daily activities, and overall quality of life. As an athlete, he tore both ACLs playing college and semi-professional football. This experience made him acutely aware of the struggles associated psychologically post-ACL injury and how to overcome them with positive results.

Visit https://keagenhadley.com/ for more information.

Made in the USA
Columbia, SC
22 April 2024